SCHOLASTIC
COLLECTIONS

Compiled by Alan Brown

D1193324

Drama & Short Plays

© 1993 Scholastic Ltd

7 8 9   9 0 1 2

Published by Scholastic Ltd,
Villiers House,
Clarendon Avenue,
Leamington Spa,
Warwickshire CV32 5PR

Compiler Alan Brown
Editor Juliet Gladston
Series designer Joy White
Designer Keith Martin
Cover and illustrations Jane Gedye

Designed using Aldus Pagemaker
Processed by Salvo Design and Print, Leamington Spa
Artwork by David Harban Design, Warwick

British Library Cataloguing-in-Publication Data
A catalogue record for this book is
available from the British Library.

ISBN 0-590-53093-3

Contents

ME AND YOU

PAST TIMES

OUR WORLD

WORK AND PLAY

MYTHS AND LEGENDS

MAKE-BELIEVE

Acknowledgements

**The publishers gratefully acknowledge permission
to reproduce the following copyright material:**

'April Fool' by Dennis Andersen from *Instructor's Big Book of Plays*, © 1983 by Scholastic Inc, all rights reserved; © 1993 Alan Brown for 'Billy', 'Opposites', 'Get home safe!' and 'Robin Hood'; © 1993 Liz Cashdan for 'Sisters'; © 1993 Debjani Chatterjee for 'Nowhere to go'; Viking Children's Books for 'The Gerbil's Funeral' and 'On a Monday morning' © 1988 June Crebbin from *The Jungle Sale*; © 1989 Berlie Doherty for 'Children of Winter' first adapted for BBC Radio 4 from the novel published by Methuen; © Scholastic Publications Ltd for 'Camping out', 'Stuck!', 'Ten in a bed', 'Past and present', 'The old suitcase', 'The broken window', 'Hats off/hats on' and 'Party guests' by Christina Dove; © 1993 Gina Douthwaite for 'Time to make friends'; © 1993 Vinata Godbole for 'The nectar of life'; © 1993 Helen Dunmore and Philip Gross for 'The Nameless Nothing from Nowhere'; © 1993 Nigel Grimshaw for 'The babes in the wood', 'The pet' adapted from *Read and Write: Book Two* published by Cassell (1983), 'The old house' and 'The shed' adapted from *Read Around: Six Easy Plays to Read or Record* published by Edward Arnold (1983); © 1993 Paul Groves for 'Street tricks' and 'Mr Egbert Nosh'; Methuen for 'Half a team' © 1993 Michael Hardcastle from *Half a Team*; © 1993 Paul Hartley for 'The time top'; © 1993 Trevor Harvey for 'Telling tales'; Longman for 'Loneliness mime' © 1993 Mike Hoy from *An Alternative Assembly Book*; © 1993 Tony Jones for 'Down to Earth' first written for Proper Job Theatre Projects, Huddersfield, and 'Small wonder' first written for Armchair Puppet Theatre, Totnes; © 1993 Kay McManus for 'The stranger in the group' and 'Rumpelstiltskin'; © 1993 Ian McMillan for 'The turning year'; © 1993 Jenny Melmoth for 'The legend of Philemon and Baucis'; © 1993 Trevor Millum for 'Lively Lou and Lazy Lynn', 'The Dark Avenger' and 'Egg quest'; Nelson for 'Duet' © Trevor Millum from *Warning, Too Much Schooling Can Damage Your Health*; © 1993 Christine Morton for 'Dragon hunt'; © 1993 Brian Moses for 'Well, what happened?' first published in *The Day the Animals Talked* published by Oxford University Press; © 1993 Maggie Norton for 'Acceleration gravytrain rap' and 'The great egg wheel do-it-yourself play'; 'The caterpillar', 'The clock' and 'The marching band' by Carol Ann Piggins from *Instructor's Big Book of Plays*, © 1983 by Scholastic Inc, all rights reserved; © 1993 Nick Pollard for 'The new invention' and 'At the market'; © 1993 Barbara Roberts for 'Helping at home', 'Who wins in a civil war?' and 'Noah's Ark'; © 1992 Anna F. Simon for 'Marcus and the hare', 'The innkeeper's tale' and 'Ling Soo and the Golden Bird'; © 1993 Ian Souter for 'Actions speak louder than words!'; © 1993 Mandy Sutter for 'The bus stop' and 'The three daft articles'; © 1993 Anna Taylor for 'The golden touch'; © 1993 Charles Thomson for 'Space ship', 'Developments' and 'The collision'; Oxford University Press for 'Whose is it?' © 1988 Charles Thomson from *Another First Poetry Book* compiled by John Foster; © 1993 Doreen Towne for 'On board ship' and 'Persephone'; © 1993 Hazel Townson for 'The lost ring', 'Prize surprise' and 'Willie's wallet'; © 1993 Tony D.Triggs for 'Clues in the ground', 'Time to go' and 'The blacksmith and the carpenter'; © 1993 Child's Play (International) Ltd for 'He'd better pay up' based on their picture book *Fisherman Fred*, published in 1994; Marshall Cavendish for 'Kind King Peter', © 1985 John Walsh from *Little Story Teller No. 1*; © 1993 Dave Ward for 'Any old rags!'; Pan Macmillan Children's Books for 'Untitled bottles' © Dave Ward from *Poems for Oxfam*; © 1993 Keith West for 'The sleepers of Thorb'; © Brenda Whitelock for 'The invitation'; © 1993 Heather Cawte Winskill for 'The Good Samaritan', 'Robots' and 'Victorian music hall'.

Every effort has been made to trace copyright holders. The publishers apologise for any inadvertent omissions.

INTRODUCTION

Most children love drama. Through drama they can increase their communication skills, extend their vocabulary and explore narrative and plot. The many writers who have contributed to this collection know that drama is a powerful way of helping children express themselves and grow in confidence. And as teachers you will know from your own experience just how effective drama can be in teaching right across the curriculum.

Scholastic Collections: Drama and Short Plays gathers together many different drama ideas and scripts. These provide ample scope for giving your children all the opportunities that drama affords. These pieces are organised under six themes encompassing many popular classroom topics. The themes range from the reality of the here and now, as in 'Me and you' to fantasy as in 'Make-believe'.

The individual pieces within each theme are further divided. First, there are scenarios where the outlines of short simple stories are told for the children to act out. The children can make up their own dialogue and movements to fit the plot. These scenario pieces can be used at all levels and are particularly helpful when working with very young children.

The next category of drama is placed under the heading improvisations. Improvisations are similar to the scenarios described previously, but instead of providing the whole story, children are given a basic situation and should then, through drama, explore the various possible outcomes of the situation and develop it using their own experiences and vivid imaginations. As with scenarios, the children can improvise their own dialogue and mimes.

For both scenarios and improvisations the minimum of props are needed. However, where certain objects are necessary these have been indicated in the text.

The remaining two categories offer more structured pieces under the headings 'Dramatic poems and dialogues' and 'Scripted drama.' The poems and dialogues can be used in a number of ways. They can simply be read out in class by one or many voices or used for choral speaking. Either way, children can use mime to accompany the pieces, either following the instructions provided in the text (where appropriate) or making up their own movements and sound effects. The children may also like to use percussion instruments to accompany pieces where this is appropriate.

Scripted dramas can be produced as simply or as lavishly as you want. As with the poems and dialogues they can be read out in class or staged as full performances including props, scenery, costumes and sound effects. (Suggestions for all of these are provided in the text.)

All the types of drama provided in this collection can be photocopied for use in the classroom. Therefore, whichever way you decide to use the pieces, all your children will be able to have access to instructions and dialogue.

All the different types of piece in this book are indexed, according to category, topic and suitable age range at the end of the book to make it even easier to find the right piece for your class and teaching plan.

Drama is obviously helpful in relation to the English curriculum especially for attainment targets on speaking and listening, reading and writing. However, drama can play an equally important part in other areas of the curriculum and this is reflected in the choice of themes in this book. Drama is explicitly recommended in the National Curriculum for developing creative imagination in science and technology and in history. Both these areas are covered in the sections 'Our world' and 'Past times'. Other sections have themes which reflect the power of drama in individual and social learning, and for experiencing through role play the adult world of work, and the otherwise unreachable worlds of legend and fiction.

If you have had little drama experience but are enthusiastic, it is important not to be too ambitious initially. Begin slowly by choosing simple pieces from among the scenarios and improvisations. You can then organise your class into groups and let each group perform to the rest of the class. (Remember that material for younger children often also works very well with older children too.) Develop a questioning approach in the children. They should be encouraged to ask themselves how particular people would react in particular situations. It is also important to bear in mind that to enable children to put themselves in the place of a character – the essence of role play – you will need to involve the class in prior work about the background to the drama.

Having worked on scenarios and improvisations, you may begin to feel confident enough to move on to working on more formal pieces. Make a game out of rehearsals. Find a part for everyone, even if it is a non-speaking one or playing a member of a crowd. Poor readers or speakers may particularly enjoy being part of a chorus where they are carried along by their friends and will gain fluency in the process. Before long you will find that drama has become a reliable part of your lesson plans and yet another of your teaching skills.

Other titles from Scholastic

The following books from Scholastic Publications provide
further support on how to work with drama.

Teacher Handbooks: Putting on a Performance by Peter Morrell.
Practical Guides: English by Bill Laar, Liz Laycock and Lyn Watkins.
Inspirations for Speaking and Listening by Alistair Ross.
Bright Ideas Drama by Alistair Ross, Jane Fulford and Helen Schmitz
Bright Ideas for Early Years: Role Play and Drama by Chris Heald

ME AND YOU

Scenarios

The lost ring

Setting

A kitchen in a family house and a picnic site.

Characters

Mum; Dad; several children.

Scenery and props

A table; a tablecloth; items for a picnic such as vacuum flask, cups, plates, sandwich boxes, food; a large picnic bag; a ring; a waste bin; chairs.

Production notes

This scenario is based on a familiar domestic situation and is particularly suited to infant and lower primary age groups. The children could be encouraged to improvise dialogue similar to the suggestions given in italics.

Scene 1

Dad is at the table, cutting sandwiches. Mum is washing fruit at the sink. The children are all helping to pack a picnic bag. As they work, they chat to one another about what they are doing *(Pass me the butter. How many cups do we need?)* and about where they will go for the picnic. *(Into the woods? Off to the seaside? Up the hill? Down to the river?)*

When the picnic bag is packed, Mum gasps with horror. She has lost her ring. She took it off to wash the fruit and now it has disappeared. A search begins and the children turn out the bin, shake the tablecloth, look under the chairs, and so on, but the ring is not found. At last Mum says that they must start the picnic without it. She will look for it later.

Scene 2

Everyone is sitting on the ground, with the picnic set out on the cloth. They start eating and drinking. They are enjoying themselves, but keep mentioning the ring. *(Where can it be? What a shame Mum has lost it.)*

Then one child gives a shriek. She has bitten something hard. The ring is inside her sandwich!

Hazel Townson

The Good Samaritan

Setting

A street.

Characters

An elderly person; two muggers; a business executive; a model; a school child.

Scenery and props

Shopping bags; a briefcase; a portable phone; a hand mirror.

Production notes

This scenario would work well in an assembly. To minimise stage-fright, the children could be encouraged to improvise dialogue along the lines given in italics.

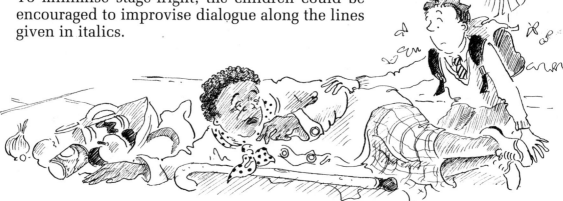

An elderly person, heavily burdened with shopping, slowly makes his/her way across the performance area. Two muggers appear running behind him/her, mug him/her and run off, possibly with one telling the other that someone is coming. The elderly person is left lying on the ground.

A business executive enters (smartly dressed, holding a briefcase and talking into a portable phone) and walks past. The elderly person calls out, but the executive makes excuses and hurries on. *(I have no time to stop. I am on my way to a meeting.)* The business executive exits, still talking into the phone.

Next, a model passes, preening him/herself in a mirror. The elderly person calls out again, but the model explains why he/she cannot stop. *(I am on my way to a shoot and I don't want to get messy.)* The model exits.

Lastly, a child, identifiable as a member of the school, appears and goes up to the old person, asking what is wrong. He/she explains about the mugging, and is helped up by the child, who lends an arm for support. The elderly person is grateful but a little surprised. *(I didn't think that school children could be so helpful.)*

Heather Cawte Winskill

The stranger in the group

Setting

An outdoor play area.

Characters

Two groups of children with a main character in each group.

Scenery and props

Two sets of different coloured badges, enough for one badge per child; drums; torches; an umbrella; a coat; a box such as a shoe box.

Production notes

The following scenario could be adapted for use with any age group, but is probably most appropriate for use with nine- to twelve-year-olds.

The class should be divided into two groups, 'A' and 'B'. Each group should have its own badge colour to identify its members.

This scenario demonstrates how a newcomer, with some kind of different feature from the group he/she is trying to join, is distrusted and rejected because of that difference.

All the members of 'A' group are playing happily in small groups, but when a stranger from 'B' group tries to join in, they reject him/her, laughing at his/her different badge. Then someone trips over and is hurt. Although the stranger is not to blame, all the children gang up and chase him/her away.

Group 'A' resumes its games. Then one by one, the children leave for home, until there is only one remaining child. A storm begins with crashing of thunder *(drums)* and lightning *(torch flashes)*. The lone child from 'A' is afraid and crouches somewhere to shelter.

The stranger from 'B' returns carrying an umbrella and a coat. He/she offers them to the lone child from 'A' and leads him/her away to his/her own home.

Here, among the children from group 'B', the lone child from group 'A' is now the newcomer and stranger. He/she tries to join in their games, but they laugh and tease him/her because of his/her different badge. Realising now what the stranger from 'B' must have felt before, he/she goes off and returns with his/her own group. The two children from 'A' and 'B' try to organise their friends into mixed groups, but everyone wants to stay with their own kind, and it all proves hopeless.

Finally, the two children from 'A' and 'B' go into a huddle – and return with a box. Very deliberately, they take off their badges and drop them into the box, inviting both groups to do the same.

At last it is no longer possible to distinguish between the two groups. Delighted, they move into a big circle and begin to dance.

There are no longer any differences or strangers.

Kay McManus

Improvisations

The first four of the following improvisations are suitable for use with younger age groups while the rest are for junior pupils and those who have developed reading fluency. The class could be divided into groups and given one of the situations to improvise. Possible ideas and suggestions are given in italics.

The shed

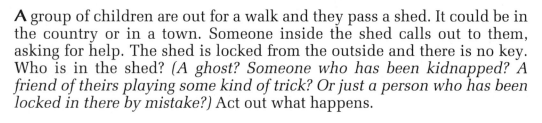

Setting

Outdoors.

Characters

A group of children.

Scenery and props

A place where a child could hide, such as a table or a door.

A group of children are out for a walk and they pass a shed. It could be in the country or in a town. Someone inside the shed calls out to them, asking for help. The shed is locked from the outside and there is no key. Who is in the shed? *(A ghost? Someone who has been kidnapped? A friend of theirs playing some kind of trick? Or just a person who has been locked in there by mistake?)* Act out what happens.

Nigel Grimshaw

Camping out

Setting

A campsite.

Characters

A group of children.

Scenery and props

Chairs and a large sheet for making a tent; cooking utensils; rucksacks (optional); firewood; other camping equipment.

A group of children arrive at a campsite for an overnight camping trip. They must work co-operatively to pitch the tent, build a fire and cook their dinner. What do they do in the evening? *(Sit around the campfire and sing songs – or tell ghost stories?)* Act out what they do.

Christina Dove

The old house

Setting

An old empty house.

Characters

A group of children.

Some children in the group want to explore an empty old house. They have heard tales that it is haunted. Others scoff at this. At least two children say that they would be trespassing and that going into an old house could be dangerous. After an argument, some or all of the group go in. Is there anyone in there? *(A ghost? Squatters? Someone who looks after the place?)* Does whoever they find turn out to be rather nasty? Or does the person need help? Or is there a broken stairway or crumbling floorboards which cause an accident? Talk about what you think will happen and then act it out.

Nigel Grimshaw

Stuck!

Setting

A lift in a department store.

Characters

Mother and two children; a young man and his girlfriend; an elderly man. Other characters can be added as the size and purpose of the group demand.

A group of shoppers enter the lift at the ground floor and push the buttons for the floors that they require. The lift doors close and the lift starts to move upwards. Suddenly it stops with a jerk but the lift doors do not open. It has stuck in-between floors. How do the different people react? *(Do they start to panic? Are they calm? Do they moan about the hold up?)* Does anyone have a plan? Who decides what they should all do? How long does it take for them to be rescued? Act out what happens.

Christina Dove

Helping at home

Setting

A family home.

Characters

Mum; Dad; Gran; Child 1; Child 2.

Scenery and props

Chairs; a table; a telephone.

Production notes

The main aim of this improvisation is to give children the experience of a point of view which is different from their own. The character briefs should be given out so that each child in a group has a different one. The situation information should only be given to the child indicated.

Mum

You have burned your left hand. The pain in your hand means that you can't sleep at night. You can't work as a cleaner and are therefore not paid. You have not got much food in the house.

Dad

You work at a factory but might soon be on short time. You are kind and cheerful, and you like football and TV. You want to bring some friends round to watch a match.

Gran

You live with your daughter and her husband who, in your opinion, is not good enough for her. You think your grandchild isn't doing well at school and blame the father for not taking enough interest. You can't walk far and complain that the house is always cold.

Child 1

You are conscientious and try hard at school, but find the work difficult. You don't like your gran but love your mum. You have one friend who lives a distance away whom you phone for help or a chat when you can.

Child 2

You are the older child and family favourite, clever and dutiful. You have left school. You are earning, but not contributing either money or help for the rest of the family.

The situation (to be given to Child 1)

You have been in trouble at school for not finishing your homework and it must be done tonight. However, you have promised to help your mother with the housework and the shopping. You need £2 for a school trip.

Barbara Roberts

The bus stop

Setting

A bus stop.

Characters

Three girls and three boys.

Scenery and props

Something to represent a bus stop (such as a coat stand); outdoor clothes.

Scene 1

Two girls are standing at a bus stop, chatting about going out, school, friends and so on. The bus is late and Girl 1 worries that they will still be waiting even after it gets dark. Boy 1 approaches, saying he's homeless and asking them for money. They try to ignore him, but he persists, telling them a convincing sob story. Girl 2 starts talking to him and eventually gives him some money. Girl 1, who won't have anything to do with him at all, is horrified. She is furious with Girl 2 for giving him money.

Boy 1 leaves and Girl 1 and Girl 2 argue furiously. At first, they simply accuse each other *(You're mean! You're a soft touch!)* but then they begin to own up to the way the incident has really made them feel, and talking about the feelings behind their differing points of view. *(Improvise dialogue to draw out how the girls might feel and why. For example, Girl 1 might say that her mum has told her a lot of scary stories to prevent her talking to strangers. Girl 2 might say she feels really sorry for people with no money because her dad was out of work and got really depressed.)*

There's no 'answer' to the situation, but talking about feelings diffuses the argument. The girls may agree at the end, or they may not.

Scene 2

Girl 3 and Boy 2, chatting together, join the bus queue. They stand and wait. Boy 3 approaches them, and tries to chat up Girl 3. Boy 2, taking a protective attitude, tries to see off Boy 3. Boy 3 will not leave and Boy 2 threatens to fight him. At this point, Girl 3 intervenes. She is angry with Boy 2, feeling she can stand up for herself and that it is none of his business whether she talks to Boy 3 or not. Boy 2 argues his point.

Girl 1 and Girl 2 meanwhile look on. They may join in and take sides if they wish to, but should not dominate the action. Boy 3 capitalises on the disagreement between Boy 2 and Girl 3 to chat up Girl 3 again. Fed up, Girl 3 finally walks away from both of them and joins Girl 1 and Girl 2. All three girls decide to walk home together and go off, leaving the boys at the bus stop.

How well the six characters know each other is a matter for discussion, either by the players or the class in a group discussion. Who has met whom before? Who knows each other well? Perhaps none of them has met previously at all. How do the incidents make each of them feel?

Mandy Sutter

Dramatic poems and dialogues

Ten in a bed

Characters

Ten children.

Scenery and props

PE mats and cushions; percussion instruments (optional).

Production notes

The children can act out this traditional song as they sing it. Use the PE mats and cushions to represent a bed. Choose the smallest child to play the little one. One by one the children should roll away to leave the little one alone in the bed. Other children can accompany the song with percussion instruments making a loud 'bang' together as each child falls out of the bed.

All: There were ten in the bed and the little one said...

Little one: Roll over, roll over.

All: So they all rolled over and one fell out. There were nine in the bed and the little one said...

Little one: Roll over, roll over.

All: So they all rolled over and one fell out. There were eight in the bed and the little one said...

Little one: Roll over, roll over.

All: So they all rolled over and one fell out. There were seven in the bed and the little one said...

Little one: Roll over, roll over.

All: So they all rolled over and one fell out. There were six in the bed and the little one said...

Little one: Roll over, roll over.

All: So they all rolled over and one fell out. There were five in the bed and the little one said...

(Continue in this way until there are only two left in the bed.)

All: So they all rolled over and one fell out. There was one in the bed and the little one said...

Little one: Now I can get some sleep!

Christina Dove

Lively Lou and Lazy Lynn

Characters

Three children, two of whom should be girls.

Production notes

In this poem for three voices, the different parts are indicated by a change in typeface. The poem is suitable for use with children aged eight and upwards.

Lively Lou and Lazy Lynn.
Were each the other's identical twin
Each wore different coloured clothes
But they weren't as different as some supposed...
Lively Lou *and Lazy Lynn*
One went out *and the other stayed in*
One got up *and the other sat down*
One gave a smile *and the other gave a frown*
One made her bed *and the other made a mess*
One wore jeans *and the other wore a dress*
One liked jam *and the other liked cheese*
Lazy Lynn *and her twin Louise.*

But sometimes just to cause confusion
They'd carry out a small illusion:
Lou stayed in *and out went Lynn*
Lou was quiet *and Lynn made a din*
Lou would scowl *and Lynn would grin.*
Is Lynn Lou or is Lou Lynn? Who knows
Which one is wearing which one's clothes?
So, when someone commits a little sin...
Well

No one knows which identical twin!

Trevor Millum

Whose is it?

Characters

Two children.

Production notes

The two speakers in this dialogue are arguing over an unspecified object.

A:	This is my one!
B:	No, it's not!
A:	It is! It's the one I got!
B:	No, it isn't – look here! See....
A:	It's the one that was given to me.
B:	It isn't yours: I can show....
A:	It's mine! It is! I know!
B:	Don't pull – it's not very strong!
A:	I want it. I'm right – you're wrong.
B:	It's yours. Look: it's broken in two.
A:	It's not mine: it belongs to you.

Charles Thomson

Untitled bottles

Setting

A market-place.

Characters

Narrator; four women; husband; children; stall-keeper.

Scenery and props

A table; several bottles filled with different coloured water; a stone.

Production notes

This drama can be used with children aged eight and upwards. Although only one narrator is indicated, the different verses could be spoken by different children. The other characters should mime the action without speaking. The children can discuss the situation. For example, if the bottles only contain coloured water, why do they have such an extraordinary effect?

Each of the bottles is filled with water.
This is important to remember.
They may bear different names on the labels.
They may appear to be different colours.
But each of the bottles is filled with water.

They stand in a line on a stall
in the far corner of the market.

The first woman comes,
and buys one of the bottles.
She thinks the bottle contains wine.
She takes it home to drink with her husband.
They end the night tipsy with ecstasy, falling
into each other's arms.

The second woman comes,
and buys the second bottle.
She think the bottle contains perfume.
She takes it home and sprinkles it
on her arms and on her neck.
She smiles at the men who smile at her,
thinking they can smell the scent
that she cannot smell.

The third woman comes,
and buys the third bottle.
She thinks the bottle contains medicine.
She takes it home and gives a spoonful
to each of her sick children.
The next day their eyes are laughing
as they sing and play in the street.

The fourth woman comes,
and asks for water.
The stall-keeper shrugs and points at the labels.
The woman unscrews the largest bottle, the one
with the water dyed the most exotic colour,
the one with the highest price on the label.

'I'll take this one,' she says, and stands
where she is and drinks every drop.
The stall-keeper, brazen-faced, still
asks for his money.
The woman bends down and picks
     up a stone.
'Here is a loaf of bread,' she says.

Dave Ward

Loneliness

Characters

Thirteen readers; the rest of the class to perform the mime.

Production notes

This dramatic poem can be used effectively as part of an assembly by junior-aged pupils. Background music such as the Beatles' 'Eleanor Rigby' could be used. The piece lends itself to simple mime which the children could improvise as suggested in italics.

Reader 1:   Alone
An island
Unconnected
Untouched

(Single pupil enters from stage left and wanders around the stage.)

Reader 2:   I am safe
Independent
I cannot be rejected
I cannot be hurt

(Groups of pupils enter from both sides and walk amiably together, then stand and chat. One child is playfully teased.)

Reader 3:   Yet they are together
Enjoying each other
They cry and are comforted;
They share their laughter
They touch

(Single pupil walks enviously past groups. One member is comforted by another and then they laugh and hug.)

Reader 4:   I need others
I must make contact
They do not see me
They do not hear me
I increase my efforts

(Single pupil approaches others with faint smile and half-hearted wave. Then walks forward with determination, stretching out hand in greeting.)

Reader 5:   I'm real
I can talk and laugh
I can cry and touch
I am not alone

(Single child mimes talking to group. They listen, smile and nod. One member clasps his/her shoulder. They walk off amiably.)

Reader 6: Being on your own is not the same as being lonely. You can be happy on your own. We all need some space to spend some time with ourselves.

(Whole group mimes something they may do alone which they enjoy such as a hobby.)

Reader 7: But we also need people. Loneliness is wanting to be with other people but not being able to reach them.

Reader 8: We can reach others in many ways. There are people who cannot walk, talk, see, or hear but who still live happy lives.

(The class act out people with disabilities successfully relating to others.)

Reader 9: Old people are often lonely. Almost every city or town has many old people living alone and isolated.

(Half the class act out the part of lonely, elderly people. The rest of the class rush about being busy with each other.)

Reader 10: But it is not just old people who are lonely. All of us can be desperately lonely sometimes.

(The children who have been rushing about stop suddenly and spread out to emphasise their isolation. The elderly group also stop.)

Reader 11: If you are lonely it will be because you lack the confidence to join in with things that other people are doing.

(Both groups turn to look at each other.)

Reader 12: It can be a great effort to talk to people *first* or to ask to join in with what they are doing in case they say no.

(One by one each member of each group stretches a tentative arm out to a member of the other group.)

Reader 13: If you show interest in other people and what they're doing and if you ask them questions about themselves, they'll nearly always be happy to talk to you. Most other people you meet are probably wanting to make friends as well.

(The pairs walk towards each other slowly and as they meet they join hands.)

All: Let us remember that we are all different. Let us remember to include in our talk and our games not just popular people but also those who may still want friends. Let us remember that everyone we meet is unique and special.

(The pairs form an inner and outer circle, still joining hands. The inner circle moves round and as each meets a new partner they join hands.)

Mike Hoy

Duet

Characters
Two boys.

Production notes
The lines in this dramatic poem, although spoken by two voices, belong to the same boy and this needs to be made apparent, perhaps in the way in which the boys are dressed or in the way they stand.

Once upon a time
last week

In a dark dank castle yard
our playground

Stood a modest misty-eyed maiden
our Vicky

In the grip of a scaly spotted serpent
Wayne Smith

And its oily orc-like allies.
Ian and Alan

The valiant virile warrior
me

Strode straight through the mighty portal
the school gates

Bearing his sharp and shiny sword and dagger
compass and ruler

And roaring, 'Avaunt ye miscreants and malefactors!'
Oi you!

'Unhand yon pure and matchless maid upon the instant!'
Geroff our Vicky

There ensued a bloody bruising battle
a big scrap

Which will be remembered in the great tales of heroic deeds:
till next week

But then the clamorous din diminished
it went quiet

And they cowered in the shadow of an even mightier and more menacing monster
the Head

Whose nostrils breathed forth fire and eyes flashed most fearsome.
he was not pleased

Incarcerated in a grim and gloomy dungeon
his office

The warrior was fearless in the just denunciations of the evil trio:
I blamed them

'I saved her from their low and loathsome clutches,' quoth he.
I showed off

The monstrous fire-breathing eye-flashing form demandeth, 'Be there yet truth in this, O damsel?'
is he right?

The warrior lifted his noble head proudly; he would be not merely saved, but honoured!
I was confident

Quoth she, 'Not one jot, O noble lord.'
NO
eh?

And declared in roundest terms the scaly spotted serpent was her beloved!
Wayne Smith was her boyfriend!

The warrior was wan, discomfitted, forlorn...
I was fed up

And swore an awesome, mouth-filling, teeth-grinding, toe-curling oath to be avenged!
Just wait till our mum hears about this!!!

Trevor Millum

Scripted drama

Actions speak louder than words!

Setting
A family house.

Characters
Michael; Mum; Dad; Gran.

Scenery and props
Bed covers; bowls and cereal packets; tatty newspaper.

Michael: My name's Michael and sometimes in my family actions speak louder than words. What I mean is that we don't like to waste time, and so we never seem to finish what we're saying. Look, you'll soon see what I mean but I'd better get back into bed because Mum's just about to go into her usual early-morning-get-out-of-bed-NOWconversation!

Mum: Michael, are you getting...?

Michael: Yes Mum, I'm just....

Mum: Well, you'd better....

Michael: Mum, can't I...?

Mum: No because it's already....

Michael: But...!

Mum: Michael, if you don't....

Michael: But it's only....

Mum: If you don't get down here I'll....

Michael: But...!

Mum: Michael, stop BUTTING in and just get yourself....

Michael: Coming Mum!

(Two minutes later and Michael is STILL in bed!)

Mum: MICHAEL!

(Michael leaps out of bed and sprints for the bathroom.)

Michael: Coming Mum, I'm....

Mum: If you're not down by the time I count....

Michael: Just washing my....

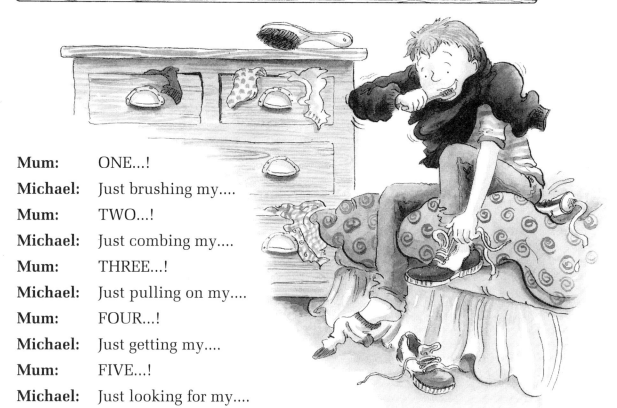

Mum: ONE...!

Michael: Just brushing my....

Mum: TWO...!

Michael: Just combing my....

Mum: THREE...!

Michael: Just pulling on my....

Mum: FOUR...!

Michael: Just getting my....

Mum: FIVE...!

Michael: Just looking for my....

Mum: If I get to six you're going to be in big....

(Michael kangaroos down the stairs and arrives in the kitchen.)

Michael: Made it and just in....

Mum: TIME! Now what do you want for....

Michael: Breakfast? Oh, just my usual! SNAP! CRACKLE! and....

Mum: STOP!

Michael: Stop? But I haven't started....

Mum: Stop because have you tidied your....

Michael: Oh Mum, I'll do it....

Mum: Yes, well, straight after breakfast and there'll be no....

Michael: Dillydallying!

(Dad now drifts into the kitchen.)

Dad: Good....

Mum: Morning.

Dad: Has anybody seen the...?

Mum: Paper! Yes....

Dad: Don't tell me. Hoover has....

Mum: Yes, he was first to the door again. You should....

Dad: Lock that dog up and....

Michael: But you know he likes reading the....

Dad: Sports pages! Yes, and I suppose he's decorated the....

Mum: Lounge with it.

(Dad goes out to collect what is left of the morning newspaper and Gran then arrives. She has problems with her memory!)

Gran: Good morning, and before you say anything has anyone seen my er, er...?

Mum: Spectacles? They're on your....

Michael: Head, Gran.

Gran: Oh, how stupid. I am so....

Michael: Forgetful!

Mum: And you my lad are so....

Gran: Untidy! Now look you've got me doing it and....

Mum: Got you doing...?

(Dad comes back in carrying what's left of the morning newspaper.)

Dad: Look at these pages and I can't find the....

Michael: Sports section?

Gran: Look, you're at it again!

Dad: At....

Mum: What again, Mum?

Gran: Taking the words right out of each other's mouths and I'll tell you one....

Michael: Thing!

Gran: Thank you, Michael, but I *can* manage on my own and before anyone says another word in this house, I'm going to finish my sentence with an important announcement which is that – today....

Dad: Yes?

Gran: I'm, er....

Mum: Go on, Mum!

Gran: Going to, er... er... er....

Michael: To, er, what Gran?

Gran: Botheration, I can't....

All: REMEMBER!

Ian Souter

The invitation

Setting

Mayor's office and a school.

Characters

Narrator; Mayor; Secretary; Teacher; children; parents.

Scenery and props

Letters; diary; apron; table; cooking pot; various types of vegetables; items of clothing from various national costumes; mayoral robes; bowls; spoons; large sheet of paper; felt-tipped pen.

Production notes

The vegetable each child provides should represent a different country chosen by them or the teacher. The children can also wear part of the appropriate national costume.

Scene 1

(The Mayor is sitting in his office. His secretary is with him. They are busy opening envelopes and reading the letters.)

Narrator: A new school is soon to celebrate its official opening. Invitations have been sent out and an air of excitement is building as the day gets closer. One very special invitation has been sent to the Mayor.

Mayor: Nothing interesting in the post this morning, just bills and complaints. I want something exciting. Something to get my teeth into. Mayors are supposed to open things, to get invited out to tea or lunch, and to make important speeches.

Secretary: This looks promising, Mr Mayor. It's an invitation to open a new school. *(Reads a bit more.) And* an invitation to make a speech. *(Reads a bit more.) And* an invitation to stay to lunch with the children.

Mayor: Let me see the invitation. *(As he reads, his grin gets bigger and bigger.)* What a nice letter. And, just fancy, they want me to stay for lunch. Have I any other commitments that day?

Secretary: *(Checks a diary.)* No, Mr Mayor, you're free all day.

Mayor: Great! *(Jumps up and claps hands.)* Then I'll accept the children's invitation. Will you write a letter on my behalf?

Scene 2

(In the classroom. Teacher is surrounded by children who are very excited, talking and laughing.)

Teacher: Hush... quiet now... calm down... silence! That's better. Did you all take your invitations home?

Children: *(Chorus.)* Yes.

Teacher: Are all your families coming to the official opening?

Children: *(Chorus.)* Yes.

Teacher: Now, the good news is that the Head Teacher has asked *me* to help prepare the lunch and our special guest will be the Very Honourable Mayor.

Children: *(Chorus.)* Hurray... great... super... *(Improvise responses.)*

Teacher: Hush... quiet now... calm down... SILENCE! That's better. And the bad news is... I can't cook.

Children: *(Chorus.)* Oh no... too bad... shame... *(Improvise responses.)*

Teacher: Hush... quiet now... calm down... SILENCE! That's better. I need to think.... Perhaps if you all helped me, we could cook a special soup. Will you help me?

Children: *(Chorus.)* Yes, yes, of course we'll help.

Narrator: And so the children and the teacher plan a simple meal. They decide that each of them will contribute something towards the soup. Each child will choose a country or culture to represent and will bring a vegetable that is native to that country or culture. The children are to wear the appropriate national costume for the big, very important day.

Scene 3

(Teacher is wearing an apron and standing beside a large cooking pot. Children, dressed in colourful costumes, are sitting down, waiting to take their vegetable to Teacher. As they hand over the vegetables, each child declares what the vegetable is and Teacher thanks them. The script provides suggestions for this and can easily be adapted.)

Child 1: A leek from Wales.

Teacher: Thank you, Wales. *(Chops up the vegetable and places it in the pot. This is repeated after each presentation.)*

Child 2: Bean sprouts from China.

Teacher: Thank you, China.

Child 3: Green beans from France.

Teacher: Thank you, France.

(Continue for each child in the group. Suggested vegetables are: plantain from the West Indies, chilli peppers from Pakistan, baby sweetcorn from Kenya, potato from Ireland and so on. When all children have given their gift of a vegetable Teacher stirs the soup and sniffs the aroma.)

Teacher: Thank you, children, this soup does smell delicious. It looks colourful... just like a rainbow.... *(Tastes soup.)* It tastes good because all the vegetables are mixed together and each one improves the other. A great melting pot of goodness. The soup needs to be cooked a little longer. Shall we sing while we wait?

Children: *(Chorus.)* Yes. *(They gather around Teacher and begin to sing. 'I can sing a rainbow' or 'Melting pot' by Blue Mink.)*

Scene 4

(This scene which takes place at the school is a mimed scene.)

Narrator: The Mayor has arrived. He is welcomed by the Head Teacher. Some of the parents are shaking his hand. He ceremoniously cuts the ribbon and declares the school officially open. Now he is coming into the school.

Scene 5

(The Mayor enters dressed in full regalia and greets children and Teacher.)

Mayor: Hello, Teacher... hello, children.

Children: *(Chorus.)* Hello, Mr Mayor... welcome to our new school.

Mayor: Thank you for asking me to open your school.

Teacher: Can we offer you some hot soup?

Mayor: Thank you, I love soup.

(Mayor takes bowl of soup offered to him by Teacher.)

Mayor: *(Tries soup.)* Lovely, rich, tasty and colourful. Just like the children. *(To children.)* Did you help to make this?

Children: *(Chorus.)* Yes. Yes we did.

Mayor: Then I must have the recipe. What's in this lovely soup?

Narrator: The Mayor sups his soup. He beams and smiles for as you can see he is a happy Mayor and he loves to eat.

Teacher: While you enjoy the soup, the children will write out the recipe for you. *(Children take turns to write down ingredients on a large sheet of paper. When recipe is finished, Teacher presents it to Mayor. Children come forward and Mayor thanks them.)*

Mayor: Thank you, children, for a wonderful day, and the recipe. Every time I make the soup I will remember you.

Brenda Whitelock

April fool

Setting

The Hooper kitchen.

Characters

Mum; Dad; Tom; Jenny; three space aliens.

Scenery and props

Kitchen table; empty cereal packets; bowls; spoons; glasses; mugs; book.

Production notes

The Hoopers can all wear modern dress. The visiting space creatures can wear anything unusual.

(Tom is sitting at the breakfast table, eating cereal. He isn't paying attention to the cereal because he's absorbed in a book.)

Jenny: *(Enters.)* Morning, Tom.

Tom: Morning, Jen.

Jenny: Gosh, that cereal looks good.

Tom: *(Hardly listening.)* Uh-huh.

Jenny: But what's that funny thing on your spoon?

Tom: *(Still reads his book.)* What funny thing? *(He swallows the spoonful.)* What are you talking about?

Jenny: Oh, no! It was a fly! You ate a fly!

Tom: What? Help! Mum! Dad! I swallowed a fly!

Mum: *(Enters with Dad.)* Now, Tom, don't worry. When you were little, you ate much stranger things. One tiny fly won't hurt.

Dad: You'll live.

Tom: I'm going to be sick.

Jenny: *(Trying to keep from laughing.)* Oh, Tom. It wasn't a fly. It was a raisin. April fool! *(Laughs and runs out of back door.)*

Mum: Honestly, I don't know what we're going to do about that child. Jenny's stories are getting out of hand. She's always stirring up some kind of trouble, April Fools' Day or not.

Dad: I've been reading about this in a book on child psychology. It says the best cure is to agree with everything the child says.

Mum: But why on earth should we do that?

Dad: If you refuse to get upset or excited about the practical jokes — the child will get tired of the game and give it all up.

Mum: I'm not so sure it would work with Jenny, but let's try.

Tom: Count me in!

Jenny: *(Enters out of breath.)* Mum! Dad! Tom! Guess what?

Mum: *(Calmly.)* What, Jenny?

Jenny: A UFO has just landed in our garden!

Dad: *(Calmly.)* That's nice, dear.

Tom: *(Calmly.)* What a shame! There go the daffodils.

Jenny: Didn't you hear what I said?

Mum: *(Begins to clear the breakfast dishes calmly.)* Of course we did, Jenny. You said a UFO landed in our garden.

Dad: And I suppose it trampled the tulips, too.

Jenny: Of course it trampled the tulips. Now what'll we do?

Mum: We'll simply have to start again from scratch.

Tom: Just as soon as the UFO takes off.

Dad: Jenny, did they tell you when they were planning to leave?

Jenny: *(Very disturbed.)* I didn't talk to anybody. I came running in here the minute I saw it.

Mum: That's good, dear. You should never to talk to strangers.

Jenny: Shouldn't we call the police?

Dad: The police? Now why would they care about our garden?

Tom: If they're not in a hurry, Jenny could invite them to breakfast.

Dad: That's a great idea.

(Jenny throws up her hands and exits.)

Dad: *(Laughing.)* See, I told you it would work.

Tom: Hey, Dad, this psychology stuff really works!

Mum: *(Looking out of the window.)* Oh my goodness. *(Stunned.)* Jenny's just invited three space aliens to breakfast.

(Dad and Tom look out the window.)

Tom: Gosh, Dad, what are we going to do?

Dad: Set out some more food for our *(Pauses.)* guests?

(Three visitors from outer space enter, sit at the table, and begin eating the cereal. Mum, Dad and Tom look stunned.)

Jenny: *(Enters smiling.)* This is the best April Fools' Day I've ever had. And all I had to do was tell the truth!

Dennis Andersen

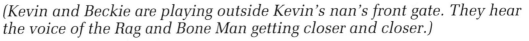

Any old rags!

Setting

Nan's front garden and the street.

Characters

Rag and Bone Man; Beckie; Kevin; Nan.

Scenery and props

Balloons; teapot; brooch; old jar; bag of marbles;
bag of toffees; handcart (improvised: trolley/chair);
seven pence; an old bus ticket.

*(Kevin and Beckie are playing outside Kevin's nan's front gate. They hear
the voice of the Rag and Bone Man getting closer and closer.)*

Rag Man: Any old rags!

Kevin: What's that noise? What's he saying? I can't hear.

Beckie: Neither can I. Hang on a minute. It sounds like 'Heavy gold
bags'. Do you think he's got bags of gold to give away?

Kevin: Don't be stupid. I can hear it now. It's 'any old rags'. He's not
giving anything away. He's collecting stuff no one wants.

(The Rag Man is still calling.)

Beckie: Like what?

Kevin: Like old clothes and china. And maybe old toys.

Beckie: I'm not giving any of my old toys away. Does he give you
anything for them?

Kevin: Not a lot. Maybe some balloons. But it's a good way of getting
rid of junk and clearing some space, my mum always says.

*(The Rag Man comes round the corner and stops with his handcart. He's
holding a fistful of balloons.)*

Beckie: Oooh! Look at the balloons. Aren't they lovely? I want one, I
want one. What can we give him?

Rag Man: Any old rags! Come on my ducks, clear out your cupboards,
and I'll give you a lovely balloon.

Beckie: I know. I've got a bag of marbles I won off Danny Brown. I
never play with them now. *(She pulls them out.)*

Kevin: I wouldn't mind them myself. Look at the colours. You've got
some winners there. They're worth more than a balloon. Tell
you what – I'll swap you. I'll give you this bag of toffees if
you'll give me the marbles.

(Beckie looks at the toffees and looks at the marbles. She's not sure.)

Beckie: But as soon as I've eaten them, they'll be gone. I'll have nothing left. But you'll still have the marbles.

Kevin: Knowing my luck, Danny Brown will win them all back anyway. And toffees taste better than marbles!

Beckie: Oh, all right. *(They swap.)*

Beckie: But I still want one of those balloons. What can we give him?

Kevin: I know. Nan's got an old cracked teapot I've never seen her use. I'm sure she'd love to get rid of that. I'll go and fetch it.

(While he's gone, Beckie unwraps a toffee. She puts the wrapper back in the bag. Kevin returns.)

Kevin: Here it is.

(The Rag Man lifts the lid and peers inside.)

Rag Man: Very nice, very nice. I'll give you two balloons.

(He hands the balloons to Beckie. Kevin is busy peering at what else is on the cart. He finds a jar, decorated with shells.)

Kevin: Look at this! It's just right to keep my new marbles in.

Rag Man: A bargain there, son. You can have it for ten pence.

(Kevin looks through his pockets.)

Kevin: Seven pence and an old bus ticket. That's all I've got. Can you lend me three pence, Beckie?

Beckie: You must be joking. You still owe me five pence from the other day.

Rag man: I tell you what, son. You can have this beautiful jar for seven pence, an old bus ticket and a balloon.

Kevin: That's fair enough. Give me one of the balloons, Beckie.

Beckie: I don't know if I should – you still owe me five pence!

Kevin: I like that! At least one of the balloons should be mine anyway. It was *my* nan's teapot we swapped, after all.

(Beckie sighs, eats another toffee and hands over the balloon. Kevin hands the balloon, seven pence and the bus ticket to the Rag Man and takes the jar. The Rag Man goes off just as Kevin's nan comes out.)

Nan: What have you been up to while I was in the back garden?

Kevin: Look, Nan, look! We got this big red balloon.

Nan: Who gave you that?

Beckie: The Rag and Bone Man.

Nan: Oh, did he now? And what did you give him?

Kevin: It was nothing – just that old teapot. The one you haven't used for years.

Nan: You mean the one with the red flowers on? I've been meaning to throw it away for ages now.

Kevin: Yes... no. No – I don't think it had red flowers on it.

Nan: Oh dear. You don't mean the blue one? I still use that.

Beckie: No – it wasn't a blue one either.

Kevin: No, Nan, no. That really old one. You never use it at all. It's all cracked and stained.

Nan: Oh Kevin! Not that one. That teapot's not just old. It's very, very old. It used to belong to my mother. I never use it because I don't want to break it, and now it's getting rattled around on the back of the Rag Man's cart. It'll be smashed to pieces by now. You just wait till I tell your mum!

Kevin: Oh, Nan, Nan, I'm sorry. I really didn't know. Listen – I know it's not much in return, but you can have this jar I just got. I was going to keep my marbles in it.

Nan: I'm sure I could use it for lots of things, but not for making tea.

Beckie: But you said you didn't make tea in that teapot.

Nan: That's not the point. Whenever I looked at that teapot, I used to think of my mother years and years ago. I could still smell her baking and hear her voice singing. Teapots hold more than tea, you know. They're full of memories as well.

(Kevin and Beckie look embarrassed. Beckie chews another toffee and Kevin rattles the jar.)

Kevin: What's this in here?

Beckie: It's some sort of funny old brooch.

Nan: Let me see. Why, that's mine! It was my mother's, too. I used to watch the firelight dancing on it every night as she told me a story before I went to sleep.

Kevin: Stories like you tell us, Nan?

Nan: Exactly the same. The stories I tell you are the stories my mother told me. When I look at this brooch, the stories come back to me. But I lost it a few weeks ago. I was wearing it at a jumble sale and it must have come unclipped.

Kevin: I wondered why some of your stories sounded different.

Nan: I know. I had to make up something new for the bits I couldn't remember. Fancy the brooch turning up in your jar!

Beckie: Maybe the jar was at the jumble sale too.

Nan: Maybe it was. Well – I feel a little bit better now. But I'd like it even more if I could get that teapot back.

(In the distance, the Rag Man's voice again.)

Beckie: Listen. I can hear him.

Kevin: I bet he's just gone round the block. Look there he is — at the other end of the street.

(The Rag Man appears. Kevin runs after him.)

Kevin: Hey, stop! We've made a mistake. My nan wants her teapot back.

Nan: If it's not all smashed to pieces.

(The Rag Man stops. They all gather round.)

Nan: My teapot! Thank goodness it's safe.

Rag Man: I look after everything I get, you know. I might get a good price for this down the market.

Nan: I'm sure you will. It used to be my mother's — and it's worth more than two balloons.

Rag Man: You're quite right there — what will you offer me for it?

Nan: I'm not offering anything at all. It's my teapot and I want it back.

Rag Man: Well, madam, I'm sure something can be arranged. I tell you what — I'll give you back the teapot if you give me the two balloons.

Beckie: That's not fair! You know we can't. We gave you one balloon back already in exchange for Kevin's jar.

Rag Man: *(Scratches his head.)* Well now — I'll have to think about this. If I let it go for one balloon, I'd be letting you off cheap. I tell you what I *really* fancy. Forget about the balloon. But I've been watching you eating that bagful of toffees. They look really delicious. How about you give them to me, young lady, and I'll give your nan her teapot?

(Beckie smiles and hands over the bag. The Rag Man tucks it into his pocket and trundles his cart away.)

Nan: Is everybody happy now? I've got my teapot back *and* I've found my brooch.

Kevin: I've got a bag of marbles and a jar to put them in.

Beckie: And I've got a balloon.

Nan: But what about your toffees? I'm afraid we lost out there.

Beckie: Oh no we didn't. I just scoffed the last one. All the Rag Man got for his troubles were the wrappers in the empty bag!

Dave Ward

Billy

Setting

Billy's home and a street.

Characters

Billy's dad; Billy Caldwell; Billy's mum; Paul; Edward; Vicky.

Scenery and props

Items for sound-effects including a bicycle with a bell, a book or magazine.

Production notes

This play was originally written for radio and therefore sound effects play an important part. The children could be allowed to record the sound effects and dialogue to make their own 'radio play' for other classes to listen to. They should be encouraged to try to achieve a 'crossfade' effect to ensure a smooth transition between scenes.

Scene 1

(Billy's home.)

Dad: Well, you're not getting another one! Not bally likely!

Billy: Dad!

Dad: Why can't you take no for an answer, Billy? Give me some peace. I gotta get a bet on.

Billy: Mum!

Mum: You heard your father, Billy. In a bit, when we're not so short...

(Billy groans.)

Mum: Now where're you off to? It's nearly dinner time.

Billy: Goin' to see Vicky and the gang.

Scene 2

(In the street are heard children laughing, bicycle bells and so on.)

Paul: You'll have to run faster than that.

(Billy pants.)

Edward: Like a Zulu warrior.

Billy: Why like a Zulu warrior?

Edward: They run everywhere.

Vicky: I think it's mean to make Billy run so fast. We should go without him.

Billy: Hey Vicky, I thought you were my friend!

Vicky: You can't be friends with somebody who hasn't got a bike. Why doesn't your dad mend it?

Billy: *(Sulkily.)* He says it can't be mended. I've bent the frame, or something. Anyway, he says he wouldn't mend it even if he could. Not till I learn to ride it proper.

Paul: It was a great smash! Heard it from my house. I thought somebody'd been killed at least! But it was only you. And there wasn't much blood.

Billy: Dad was gonna give me a good hiding for spoiling me clothes. That's not fair, is it? Me injured, me bike a wreck, and he wants to give me a good hiding!

Paul: Did he?

Billy: No.

Edward: Shame!

Vicky: How can you learn to ride it if you can't ride it?

Billy: Dunno. Said something about me learning me Highway Code.

Paul: It's on page thirty-two. Don't run into the back of parked cars!

Billy: You're not my friend, Paul!

Edward: Page fifty-four. Look where you're going'!

Billy: Neither are you, Edward!

Vicky: Page forty-three. Stay in the saddle at all times!

Billy: I hate you all!

Scene 3

(Billy's home.)

Billy: Dad!

Dad: Mmm... Double Trouble in the four o'clock. Never back the favourite, Billy. Only mugs back the favourite.

Billy: Dad! I've learned me Highway Code!

Dad: Highway what? Which race is that?

Billy: The Highway Code. You told me to learn it. You said you'd get me a new bike if I learned it. *(Pause.)* Or mend me old one.

Dad: Did I say that?

Billy: Yeah. Mum heard you.

Dad: We'll see.

Billy: I learned it all! I could drive... anything now! Go on, test me!

Dad: Hmm...

Billy: Go on, test me! Test me!

Dad: Right.

(Noise of leafing through pages.)

Billy: Yes?

Dad: Well, then. Right. What's the sequence of traffic lights?

Billy: Sequence? The sequence of traffic lights?

Dad: *(Slowly.)* The sequence of traffic lights. What comes after green?

Scene 4

(A street.)

Paul: Well, what does come after green?

Billy: Amber. No, green and amber. I dunno – I've forgotten again!

(Noise of bikes – backpedalling, clicking gears.)

Billy: Where're you goin', Paul?

Paul: We're goin' down the Damson, ride our bikes on the dirt track.

Billy: That's a long way.

Paul: Not on a bike.

Vicky: Everybody should have a bike. You can't have fun with somebody who hasn't got a bike.

Edward: Make them run, that's what you can do.

(Sounds of laughing, bicycle bells ringing.)

Vicky: Bye, Billy! Bye!

Scene 5

(Billy's home.)

Billy: Dad!

Dad: Hang on, Billy. I'm just writing this bet out. Wincanton. The three o'clock.

Billy: Dad! Mum said to tell you I did my exams today!

Dad: Your exams, Billy?

Billy: Me Eleven Plus. For the grammar.

Dad: Right! Did you pass?

Billy: I dunno! They don't mark it straight away, you know!

Dad: Now don't give me your cheek, Billy. You must know how you did, a clever boy like you. Did you do all the questions?

Billy: No, I didn't finish....

Dad: Well, that's that, then. I must say, I'm disappointed. I thought you'd do better than that.

Billy: You don't have to do all the questions. There's lots and lots of 'em. Nobody could answer 'em all!

Dad: Never mind. You'll get over it.

Billy: I might pass....

Dad: After all, you haven't lost anything, have you? You can still go to the modern like everybody else.

Billy: I don't want to go to the modern.

Dad: What's wrong with the modern? It was good enough for the rest of the family! You too good for us now, Billy?

Billy: No, it's not that....

Dad: You ashamed of your own family?

Billy: No, it's just....

Dad: Just because you got brains and we haven't?

Billy: No....

Scene 6

(Billy's home some weeks later.)

Mum: There was a letter today. From the Chief Education Officer.

Billy: It's me letter! Have I passed? Am I goin' to the Grammar?

Mum: You have a look. I couldn't make head nor tail of it.

Billy: The County Grammar School – that's the place! I'm goin' to the Grammar!

Scene 7

(A street.)

Paul: So you're goin' to the Grammar, eh Billy?

Billy: Who told you that?

Edward: We got spies everywhere.

Vicky: I don't suppose you'll want anything to do with me.

Billy: No, Vicky. I mean, yes. I mean....

Paul: Too good for us, he is. Too good for your old friends, Billy?

Edward: Your ex-friends.

Vicky:	You can't be friends with somebody who goes to the Grammar.
Paul:	Their parents take them by car. They don't have bikes, stuck up kids like that.
Billy:	They do! They got bicycle sheds! I've seen 'em!
Paul:	Humph! Must be for the teachers.

Scene 8

(Billy's home some weeks later.)

Dad:	How did you get on today, Billy?
Billy:	All right. Maths was hard. We never did stuff like that at the old school.
Dad:	We never did it at all.
Billy:	You must've! Everybody does sums!
Dad:	Oh, sums! Why didn't you say so? Of course we did sums.
Billy:	They got different names for everything at the Grammar. Like, we don't do English – we do literature and language.
Dad:	I don't know anything about them things, and neither does your mother. There's nobody in our family ever been to the Grammar but you, Billy. You're on your own now.

Scene 9

(In the street a bicycle bell is heard.)

Billy:	I got it back! I got me bike back! Look! It's good as new! Let's go down to the Damson and ride our bikes!
Paul:	Oh, we don't do that no more.
Edward:	We're goin' out on our roller skates.
Billy:	I haven't got any roller skates....
Vicky:	You can't have fun with somebody who hasn't got roller skates.
Paul:	See you, Billy.
Billy:	No, wait....
Vicky:	Bye! Billy! Bye!

(Sounds of laughing, fades into the distance.)

Alan Brown

PAST TIMES
Scenarios

On board ship

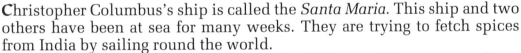

Setting

On board the *Santa Maria*.

Characters

Christopher Columbus; sailors; native Americans.

Scenery and props

Items to indicate a ship-board setting, such as ropes, barrels and nets.

Production notes

Exploration and navigation is a complex topic, but this simple storyline can be read to younger children while they mime the actions.

Christopher Columbus's ship is called the *Santa Maria*. This ship and two others have been at sea for many weeks. They are trying to fetch spices from India by sailing round the world.

A helmsman is turning the ship's wheel. Some of the crew are busy mending sails and fishing nets. Others are coiling ropes or cleaning the decks. The crew are tired and hungry for fresh food – they thought they would reach land weeks ago.

Columbus comes on deck and orders one of the sailors to climb the rigging to the crow's nest and look for land. The look-out spends a long time looking out to sea. Suddenly he/she shouts, 'Land ahoy!'

The sailors cheer. Someone brings out a pipe and they all dance for joy. Columbus orders a barrel of wine to be opened to celebrate their success.

As the ships draw near to land, Columbus and his crew see white beaches and waving green palm trees. Columbus orders small boats to be launched. Soon several groups of sailors are rowing towards the shore.

Columbus stands in the prow of the first boat. He is eager to reach land and prove that he has reached India. As he watches, Columbus sees people appear on the shore. They are warm-skinned people wearing little but grass skirts and garlands of flowers. Some are shouting in a strange language and waving their arms. Suddenly, Columbus is not so sure that he has found India after all....

Doreen Towne

Street tricks

Earlier this century the street was the main playground for children. There were few cars and they could play in safety. They played many games but when they tired of these they would often get up to tricks. Here are four for acting out.

Setting

1905: a village in Northamptonshire. A foggy night in the street by the churchyard.

Characters

Two children; lamplighter.

Production notes

In working out actions for this scene, the children could consider the following questions: How do you show fear in acting? How can you try and put on a deep voice? How can you act glee?

What would the children have done if a voice from behind another gravestone had said: 'I used to play that trick when I was alive.'?

The two children huddle behind a gravestone. Along comes the lamplighter – the man who used to light the lamps in the village streets. He carries a ladder. The children wait until he has climbed to the top of his ladder at the light by the churchyard. Then one of them says, in a deep voice: 'I used to do that when I was alive.'

The lamplighter falls down his ladder in fright and runs off down the street. The children laugh and jump up and down with glee.

Setting

1910: a street in Manchester at night.

Characters

Two children; two house owners.

Production notes

Children could consider the following questions: How do you act doing something quietly and secretly? How do you show annoyance? What would be the difference between annoyance and anger?

Often terraced houses at this time were built right up to the pavement. There were no front gardens. Two children tie a string from the door-knocker of one house to the door-knocker of the next. They then knock on one door and run away and hide. A woman answers the door, sees no one and shuts the door in annoyance thinking it is children playing 'knock and run'. This causes the door knocker on the next house to knock. A man comes to the door and sees no one. He too shuts the door in annoyance. The success of the trick depends on how many times the man and woman come to the door before noticing the string.

Setting

1920: a busy street in Leeds.

Characters

A child; at least two passers-by.

Production notes

Children could consider the following questions: How long might the people hold the rope? Would other passers-by stare at them as they hold the rope? How long might they be there? How would they act when they found out they had been tricked?

A child stands at the corner of the street where there is a house or high wall right up to the pavement. He/she is holding a long rope. He/she stops a passer-by and explains he/she is helping a builder and needs to measure the wall. Could the passer-by help by holding the end of the rope?

The child then goes round the corner and stops someone else and asks them the same thing. Each person now holds the rope but cannot see round the corner. The child slips away. The success of the trick depends on how long the two people would hold on to the ends of the rope.

Setting

1930: a pathway leading from a street to a park.

Characters

Two children; several passers-by.

Production notes

Act out the scene with several people trying to pick up the penny.

Two children hide behind a hedge. They have drilled a hole in the edge of an old big penny. They tie a thread to the coin, put it in the middle of the path and then trail the thread to the hedge. They then cover the thread with dust. They wait for someone to come along and try to pick up the penny. They then whisk it away.

Paul Groves

Clues in the ground

Setting

A plot of waste ground.

Characters

Two children; Museum Keeper; Antique Shop Owner; local residents; Librarian.

Scenery and props

A sand tray; a chalkboard; a miscellaneous collection of objects, such as a bone, an old tile, a piece of burnt wood, an old bottle, a sailor's button, a (broken) clay pipe, something inscribed with initials and a mystery object; a news report (example provided).

Production notes

Before the lesson, fill a sand tray or similar container with sand to represent a plot of waste ground. Hide small objects in the sand, avoiding anything sharp which might cause injury to searching fingers. Prepare a brief newspaper-style report which provides a plausible history for the plot of ground and hence a possible context for the items in question. Devise your own 'object clusters', choosing artefacts with an eye to their date, design and so on or use those suggested above.

The sandpit should then be placed on the floor between chalkboard drawings of houses numbered, say, five and nine. The board can also show a street name.

Through this work young children can gain a sense of the past. They can also practise deductive thinking and experience the complementarity of archaeological and historical data. Finally, they can learn to value ideas that contradict or go beyond established knowledge while distinguishing those which they can test from those they cannot.

The 'clues in the ground' approach can be adapted in various ways. For example, for greater authenticity consult a local archive and *start* with a suitable cutting or story and then build the object cluster around it.

Two children explore the piece of ground to discover clues about its past. One by one as they find most or all of the hidden objects they speculate about what they might mean. (The pace of this can be controlled by letting other children help to examine and evaluate each of the objects, perhaps in roles like Museum Keeper, Antique Shop Owner, residents at numbers five and nine.) List the children's ideas and conclusions as the action goes on. The list can include key questions such as, 'Was there once a house on this piece of ground?'

When appropriate, ask the two 'explorers' to check their ideas at the library and ask the 'Librarian' to read out the news report. Most large municipal libraries have local history archives with indexed cuttings extending back to the nineteenth century, so the Librarian's role is authentic (though the teacher has fabricated the 'cutting'). The newspaper report could be as follows:

The GAZETTE

27 July 1887

Fire destroys house

The town fire pump was used today at number 7, Elsey Road. A blaze had broken out at the home of George Biggs, a retired sailor. Mr Biggs had lived there for several years with his dog Samuel. Sadly, the town's brave fire team failed to put out the fire, which destroyed the house and killed both Mr Biggs and his dog.

This cutting suggests reasons for the burnt condition of the wood, the presence of the bone (perhaps buried by the dog) and the style of the button.

Commend the pupils for all their correct deductions or at least for making good use of the library. Highlight any compatible but *extra* ideas that occurred to the children or featured in the press report. For example, the children might have suspected that the fire was caused by careless smoking or that the bottle implied a lot of drinking.

Tony D. Triggs

Improvisations

The first three of the following improvisations are especially suitable for use with younger age groups while the last one is more appropriate for junior pupils and those who have developed reading fluency.

Past and present

Setting

A playground.

Characters

Four children – two from the present and two from a different period in the past such as the 1940s, Victorians and so on.

Scenery and props

Games from the present and the past – a frisbee and a hoop and stick.

Two children from the present day are playing a game in the playground. Suddenly they come upon two children who are also playing a game, but they are obviously from a different time in history. Can the children communicate? What do they do? Perhaps they teach each other their games? Discuss what might happen and act it out.

Christina Dove

The old suitcase

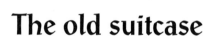

Setting

An attic.

Characters

A group of four children.

Scenery and props

An old suitcase.

A group of friends are exploring a dusty, cobwebbed attic. They discover an old, locked suitcase which has obviously not been opened for years. There is no key, but the children's curiosity is so strong that they find a way to open it. How do they do this? What do they find inside? How old are the contents? Who do they belong to? What do the children do with their find? Discuss what happens and then act it out.

Christina Dove

The time top

Setting

An antique/bric-a-brac shop in the present and various scenes (of the children's own suggestion) in the past.

Characters

A small group of children; Shopkeeper; time top; various historical characters.

Scenery and props

Items to represent the setting and contents of the bric-a-brac shop; appropriate costume and prop items for historical characters; a brightly coloured cape for the time top.

Production notes

This piece provides a simple framework for drama based on the previous history of a spinning top. The old top is discovered in a junk shop by present-day children. When they spin the top they are transported back in time to a moment in the life of one of its previous owners. This happens several times until the top spins the children back to the present. The structure of the drama and firm summaries for the first and last scenes which are set in the present time are provided. The 'historical flashback' scenes are linked by the rhymes chanted by the top as it is spun by the present-day children, and their content can be suggested and improvised by the teacher or by the children themselves using their own ideas about the past.

The following is a list of potential themes for the historical scenes and some ideas for dramatic action:
• playing in the street – street rhymes and games;
• a trip to the seaside – amusements or attitudes to bathing;
• Easter – egg painting and rolling;
• carnivals and processions – Whit walks, Wake Weeks;
• a picnic – to a local area which has since been developed;
• during a time of rapid change – 1960s or 70s, a newly immigrant family or a family relocated to a tower block;
• the Second World War – bombing raids or evacuees;
• Christmas – at the turning of the century, 1899, when the top is new.

Scene 1

(The present.)

A small group of young children pay a visit to a local bric-a-brac shop to look at the toys. Their attention is drawn to an old, brightly decorated spinning top. The Shopkeeper tells them that it has magic powers.

Although uncertain at first, the children decide to spin the top. As it spins, the top chants a rhyme.

Tick, tock, time top,
Where will I stop?
Spin me round and say the rhyme,
And I will take you back in time.

As the top comes to a halt the children find themselves watching a scene from the top's own history and the life of one of its previous owners.

Scene 2

(The first flashback.)

The children watch the scene from the past. At the end of the scene the historical characters disappear, leaving the top alone. The present-day children spin it again and are taken further back into the life of the top.

Tick, tock, time top,
Where will I stop?
Spin me once and then once more,
To see where I have lived before.

Scene 3

(The second flashback.)

This follows the same pattern as Scene 2, with the children spinning the top to go still further back – to the time when the top was new.

Tick, tock, time top,
Where will I stop?
Spin me fast, and as you do,
You'll see my face when I was new.

Scene 4

(The third flashback.)

The final flashback completes the journey back in time. The top is seen with its first owner. At the end of the scene the time top brings the children back to the present time.

Tick, tock, time top,
Where will I stop?
For the last time, spin me round,
To the place where I was found.

Scene 5

(The present.)

The children find themselves back in the shop, the top on the floor nearby. The shopkeeper knows where they have been. He/she gives the top to the children and makes them promise to look after it, so that they can pass it on to children in the future.

Paul Hartley

Who wins in a civil war?

Setting

A manor house in the seventeenth century.

Characters

The Lady of the Manor (a Royalist); her son and daughter; Anne Cope, a servant; a Roundhead officer; a second servant (optional); a Roundhead soldier (optional); a pedlar (optional).

Scenery and props

Some domestic furniture including a bed; a bag of medicine bottles.

Production notes

The children must be given sufficient background information before working on this improvisation to enable them to take up positions within the drama. For instance, they should know the stance of Cavaliers and Roundheads on the question of the monarchy, the splits that occurred in family loyalties, the difficulty of communications and the fear of informers. Some knowledge of the daily life from this time would also help to flesh out the dialogue.

The character briefs should be given out so that each child in a group has a different one. The main aim of this improvisation is to give children experience of a point of view which is different from their own. The situation brief should be given only to the child indicated.

Lady of the Manor

You are the lady of the manor house, married to a Cavalier who is away fighting and who has not been heard of for many months. You are running short of money and food, but have not told the rest of the family.

The Son of the Lady of the Manor

You are fourteen, the eldest son of a Cavalier. You want to follow your father who has gone to the war, but you are too young. You have secretly hidden one of your father's swords in your bed. You believe all Roundheads are evil.

The Daughter of the Lady of the Manor

You are the ten-year-old daughter of a Cavalier. You are very ill with fever which you bravely try to ignore for your mother's sake. You are fond of your family's old servant who cares for you.

The Servant of the Lady of the Manor

You are called Anne Cope, and have been the lifelong servant of the family and care especially for the sick daughter of the house. You are supposed to be a supporter of the King but the family do not know your son Martin has become a Roundhead.

Roundhead Officer

You are a Roundhead officer. You were serving alongside Martin Cope, the son of a servant. You are tired of the Civil War but believe in the cause of Cromwell and the end of the monarchy. You carry the medical supplies for your troops, including medicines to treat fever.

Second Servant (optional)

You are a servant for a Cavalier family. You suspect that Anne Cope, an old and trusted servant, is not wholly truthful about her support of the Cavaliers.

Roundhead Soldier (optional)

You are a soldier who follows the Roundhead officer. You demand entry to the manor house, but do not disclose your identity.

Pedlar (optional)

You are a wandering chapman (pedlar) who calls with his wares at the manor house. You might be carrying messages either from or to the armies.

The situation (to be given to the Roundhead Officer)

After a battle you became separated from your men and fall into a flooded stream. You now need food and warmth. You have lost your horse and arrive at a house where you believe your friend Martin's mother lives. You do not know who else lives there for he died before he could tell you more about it.

Barbara Roberts

Scripted drama

Marcus and the hare

Setting

The workshop of a Roman craftsman.

Characters

Narrator; Marcus, a craftsman; Fabius and Julius, his assistants; General Claudius; Metella, the General's wife; Ceres, goddess of plenty; Mars, god of war; Mercury, messenger of the gods; Venus, goddess of love and beauty; Hercules; Roman soldiers; Venus's attendants; a hare; dogs; Actaeon, a hunter; musicians.

Scenery and props

A work-bench; a bed; tools; Roman costumes; animal costumes or masks; percussion instruments.

Production notes

This one-act play for a class of seven- to eight-year-olds is based in Roman Britain and could be undertaken as part of a topic on the Romans. All the class can take part as actors or as accompanying musicians, playing percussion instruments at the side of the stage.

Narrator: In Cirencester, known as Corinium in Roman times, was found a mosaic floor, bearing the design of a hare. This play is our idea of why a hare was used in the mosaic.

(Enter Marcus and his assistants.)

Our story begins in the workshop of Marcus the craftsman. He and his men cut and shape the *tesserae* from which they construct the mosaic floors.

(Marcus examines the work of his assistants who mime cutting the tiles.)

Marcus: Very good, Fabius, but these need more work. *(Moves on to Julius.)* These will do for the 'Seasons mosaic'.

(Enter Claudius and Metella. Metella looks around disapprovingly.)

Claudius: *(Haughtily.)* Ah, Marcus.

Marcus: *(Springing round and bowing.)* General Claudius! *(Fabius and Julius bow also.)*

Claudius: Marcus, I have work for you. The building of our villa is complete except for the floor in the *triclinium*.

Metella: We cannot decide upon the design of the mosaic. Which of the gods or goddesses can we choose?

Claudius: We want you to create a design for us, Marcus.

Marcus: *(Bowing again.)* It will be an honour, General.

Claudius: Excellent! We will leave it to you. Good day, Marcus.

Marcus: Good day, General. *(Exit Claudius and Metella. Marcus, excited, still bows.)* Work for General Claudius!

Fabius: Such an important man!

Julius: But what'll you do, Marcus? What about the design?

Marcus: This is difficult. I must think hard. *(Walks towards front of stage, thinking.)* I'll choose one of the gods – but which one? *(Continues to walk up and down pensively.)*

Narrator: Marcus thought for a long while. Fabius and Julius finished work and left the shop.

Fabius/Julius: *(Together.)* Good-bye, Marcus. *(Exit Fabius and Julius. Marcus does not notice them go.)*

Narrator: Marcus thought till he was too tired to think any more. Then he lay on his bed and fell asleep. *(Marcus lies on his bed.)* As he slept, he began to dream.

(The sound of bells is heard. Marcus, dreaming, sits up slowly. Enter Ceres, carrying fruit, dancing joyfully to centre stage. Bells stop.)

Ceres: I am Ceres, the goddess of plenty. I give the summer, fine fruits and flowers, wealth and fullness. Choose me for your mosaic, Marcus, for I represent everything good.

(Ceres dances off to the sound of bells. Military drum beats begin. Enter Mars and soldiers. They march in formation across the stage and stop at the side of the stage while Mars returns to centre. Drums stop.)

Mars: I am the god of war – Mars. *(Draws sword.)* The Romans pray to me as they go into battle and I give them great victories. Choose me for your mosaic, Marcus, for I am very powerful.

(Drum beats. Exit Mars and soldiers, marching. Sound of maracas. Enter Mercury at high speed. Runs from point to point, stretching and leaping.)

Mercury: Mercury is my name – messenger of the gods. Choose me, Marcus, I'm the fastest of all. *Choose me!*

(Exits. Chime bars. Enter Venus with attendants. They sit gracefully around her as she speaks. Chime bars stop.)

Venus: Your mosaic design should be of me, Marcus, for I am Venus, most beautiful of goddesses.

(Exit Venus and attendants to schime bars. Enter Hercules to slow drum beats, flexing muscles. Drum stops.)

Hercules: I am Hercules. I have great strength, enough to carry the whole world on my shoulders. Make me your choice, Marcus. I am Hercules.

(Exit Hercules to drum beats. Marcus stands and walks to front of stage.)

Marcus: I don't know what to do!

(The gods and goddesses re-enter and circle round Marcus.)

Gods/Goddesses: *(Chanting.)* Choose me.... *(Repeat six or eight times getting louder.)*

(The hare leaps in, followed by barking dogs. Gods and goddesses leave in panic. Marcus jumps on to his bed. The dogs chase the hare till she crouches by work-bench. The dogs crouch round her, growling. She takes Marcus's hammer and threatens them with it. Enter Actaeon, swaggering.)

Actaeon: Quiet! Here! Here! *(The dogs leave the hare and come to sit round Actaeon, panting.)* I am Actaeon, the hunter. You had better choose me, Marcus, or I'll set my dogs on you!

Marcus: But you're not one of the gods. You're only a hunter. I'm not going to make a design of you!

Actaeon: *(Angrily to dogs.)* After him!

(The dogs gather round the bed. They leap at Marcus. The hare jumps out to centre stage. She whistles to the dogs. They turn to see her. She makes faces at them and then dashes off stage. They chase the hare. Exit Actaeon, calling to the dogs. Marcus, astonished, steps down from the bed, coming to the front of the stage.)

Marcus: *(Sighing.)* Thank goodness for that! I'm safe. The hare has saved me. Thank you, little hare!

(The hare appears at the side of the stage, waves cheekily to Marcus and disappears again. Marcus smiles and returns wearily to bed.)

Narrator: Marcus slept on till morning. When he awoke, he could remember the dream clearly.

Marcus: *(Rising brightly from bed and coming to centre stage.)* I've got an idea. I won't put any gods in my mosaic. I will choose the hare because she saved me from the dogs. *(Assistants return. They and Marcus start work.)*

Narrator: So Marcus and his men went to work to make the hare mosaic. General Claudius and his wife were very pleased and paid Marcus well. He gained much fame as a craftsman and all thanks to the little hare!

(Characters all return to take a bow with Marcus, assistants and narrator.)

Anna Simon

Time to go

Setting

Night time in a simple one-room home in Viking Scandinavia.

Characters

Father; Mother; Guthrum, the eldest son; Estrid, the daughter;
Eric, the younger son; Leif, an unexpected male visitor.

Scenery and props

A knife; a root of feverfew (or substitute); a chess set; a chest with purses
and money bags inside it; a few cooking utensils; simple tunics, long
dresses and cloaks.

Production notes

The play is set in Viking Scandinavia, though with minor adjustments it
could be transferred to the Germanic homeland of the Anglo-Saxons. It
examines invasion and settlement from the viewpoint of the Vikings
through the eyes of a fictional family at a time of crisis. It is suitable for
use with older children.

Father: *(Coughs, holds head and groans.)* Oh my head.

Mother: *(Places hand on his forehead.)* As hot as a furnace. *(To Guthrum, Eric and Estrid.)* Here, take this knife, someone. Go outside and get him a root of feverfew. It might help to bring his temperature down. *(Guthrum and Eric start to argue about their board game. There are cries of 'That's being greedy!', 'Cheat!' and so on.)* Guthrum, you're only playing a game – and it isn't your move. *(Tries to hand him the knife.)* Do you think you could....

Guthrum: How can I find the plants in the dark?

Mother: But they're right by the house.

Guthrum: Anyway, why should I dig up a root? It's the leaves that cure fever, not the roots.

Mother: Yes, but there's not much leaf at this time of year. Boiling roots is the best we can do.

Guthrum: And you can't do that because we've run out of firewood. *(Blows and rubs hands to keep them warm.)*

Mother: We'll manage, Guthrum. We'll burn that chest if it's all we've got. You know where they grow – at the foot of the wall. Just bring me....

Guthrum: But it's my move now. You'll have to wait.

Estrid: Father can't wait for his medicine, Guthrum. Look at the way he's shivering and sweating. *(Guthrum stamps out.)*

Mother:	*(To husband.)* It won't be long now.
Father:	No, not long. I'll be dead by the morning, as likely as not.
Mother:	I didn't mean that. I meant your medicine. But it's food you need, poor love, not medicine.
Father:	I'm so hungry it's eating my insides out. But nothing will grow in this bitter cold.
Estrid:	It's spring by the sun but it seems like winter. The snow on the hills is only just beginning to melt. *(Guthrum stamps back with a feverfew root and returns to his game.)* Eric, do you think we could eat the sheep that died? You know – the ones that died in the snowstorm.
Eric:	You mean died and got lost. How can we eat them? We never found them.
Estrid:	Oh! but haven't you noticed? In places where the snow's disappeared you can see them huddled against the walls.
Guthrum:	*(Getting up from his game.)* Where? Tell me where?
Estrid:	All over the hills. Under the walls like heaps of old snow.
Eric:	I saw them! I thought they *were* snow! I would have brought one home!
Guthrum:	I'll get one now!
Mother:	Sit down, Guthrum. Don't throw your life away!
Guthrum:	But the meat's been frozen all this while – it must be good.
Mother:	Never mind that. If you go out at night – in this wind and rain – you'll be frozen yourself.
Eric:	And you're the one who wouldn't go just outside the door to get Father some medicine.
Guthrum:	I went in the end, you liar. And while I was gone you cheated – you moved your king. You moved it an extra square.
Mother:	*(Scatters board and pieces.)* That stupid game has gone to your heads. Why is it so important to you – winning squares on a wooden board? You're behaving as if each square is a field full of oats or barley. Has hunger driven you mad or something?
Estrid:	It's greed that's driving Guthrum mad. He's thinking of all the land he'll get when Father dies.
Guthrum:	Shut up! He'll hear you!
Estrid:	Mother's right. You're playing a little pretending game and all those squares stand for Father's fields.
Guthrum:	Mother didn't say that.
Estrid:	And don't you love taking enemy pieces off the board. Enemy pieces – that's what you call them. But what are they really?

Your brothers and sisters – that's what they are. When Father dies there'll be no land for *us* to live on. We'll be like scarecrows, limping away across your fields. Or maybe you'll find us lying dead against your walls like frozen sheep.

Guthrum: Oh shut your trap.

Eric: A trap for catching birds and mice – that's all I'll have. When Father dies and brother Guthrum – big brother Guthrum – gets all the land. Why does everything have to go to the eldest?

Guthrum: That's the rule, small-fry. Anyway, why can't you start your own farm? Why can't you do what Father did? This valley was empty until he came. He wasn't afraid to scrape his hands piling boulders up to make this house. And then he spread his patchwork of fields beside the stream. And look at the hills – alive with sheep.

Eric: *(With bitter scorn.)* Alive with sheep! Hunger *is* affecting your brain.

Guthrum: All right, all right – the gods have sent us a dreadful winter. So you won't start a farm of your own because you're afraid of snow?

Eric: *(Exasperated.)* There's nowhere to do it. There's no land left.

Guthrum: *(As Leif enters.)* There's land enough below Scarcliffe Crag.

Leif: *(Taking up knife and looking menacing.)* Land for what?

Guthrum: Leif! What are you doing here at this time of night?

Leif: Looking for shelter. But ready for a fight if you want one. The swollen river stopped me getting home to my valley; I come as a friend and I find you plotting against my farm.

Eric: But we're talking about the barren land below Scarcliffe Crag.

Leif: Barren except for the farmhouse I've built. My life depends on two bags of seed and the ten sheep who are still alive in the snow.

Estrid: But you live lower down the valley – on the better land.

Leif: Not any longer. My father died and my elder brother took his farm. The rest of us have to do what we can to stay alive.

Estrid: You can still sell your pots.

Leif: *(Shaking head.)* No, I'm having to give that up. I've nowhere to make any new ones now that I've had to leave home. One day perhaps I'll build a new workshop at Scarcliffe Crag. But what's the use of being a trader? Money buys so little food in these hard times. *(Lays down knife.)* Oh, I'm sorry, you must forgive my anger; I haven't eaten properly for months.

Estrid: *(Whispering.)* It's the same with us. Look at Father. He's starving to death.

Leif: *(Shakes head despairingly.)* So what will you and Eric do when your father dies? There's no land left to start new farms.

Estrid: *(Moving over to Leif.)* Maybe I'll find a husband, Leif.

Leif: *(Moving away.)* And starve to death with him?

Guthrum: Eric can live by fishing – and carving walrus tusks – and making ropes from seal-skin and whale-skin.

Eric: Fishing? Carving? Making ropes? You must be mad. Four or five months of winter storms? Four or five months of eating dried fish? And where would I get the money to buy a fishing boat? I'll tell you something: if I had a boat I'd use it for more than fishing trips.

Estrid: What do you mean?

Eric: *(Mysteriously.)* I'd sail to the moon.

Estrid: You mean...?

Eric: *(Nodding head as if it's now a shared secret.)* I'd sail to the moon and eat the cheese.

Estrid: You mean... you'd sail west.

Eric: Till I drowned or found a valley full of honey and milk.

Estrid: Yes, but you'd need to take others with you. You'd need half the money in Father's chest to buy such a boat. *(Mother wails with grief and clasps her husband; others gather round in sorrowful acceptance. Only Guthrum stands aloof.)*

Guthrum: *(Absent-mindedly puts the playing pieces away but leaves his 'king' on the board. Goes to doorway.)* The sun's coming up. I can see it beyond the sacred tree. *(Eric tiptoes from group round his father, unlocks the family chest and removes two purses or bags of money. He quietly leaves by the opposite door from the one at which his brother is standing. Guthrum, rubbing his hands, continues to ruminate.)* Well, the worst of the frost is over. We won't have too much trouble digging Father's grave.

Tony D. Triggs

The blacksmith and the carpenter

Setting

A school in Anglo-Saxon England.

Characters

Nine pupils; teacher; a Farm-hand; Hunter; Fowler; Salter; Blacksmith; Pupil Monk; Monk; Shepherd; Fisherman; Shoemaker; the Abbot; Carpenter.

Scenery and props

No specific items are needed, but the various characters could carry objects appropriate to their trade.

Production notes

Aelfric's *Colloquy* was written over 1000 years ago. It takes the form of a playlet set in a monastery classroom. Aelfric taught in such a classroom, and he wrote his playlet to give his pupils practice in Latin.

This adaptation of Aelfric's Latin offers a glimpse of medieval life, complete with a cast of secular and religious figures who quarrel, boast or simply moan about their lives. It is suitable for use with nine- to twelve-year-olds. Although the text specifies nine pupils in the cast, this number can be increased or reduced to suit class requirements.

Teacher: We're lucky because we've got some visitors with us today. Let's ask them about the lives they lead. Shall we start with the Monk?

Monk: Yes, I'm a monk, and every day I sing the seven services with my brother monks. The first service starts so early that I have to get up in the night.

Farm-hand: It's the same for me. At dawn I drive a team of oxen into the field. I fear my master, so even in the bitterest winters I daren't stay at home. I plough at least one field a day.

Pupil 1: Do you have anyone to help you?

Farm-hand: I've a boy with a stick to drive the oxen. He's lost his voice because of the cold and all the shouting he has to do. In the evenings he helps me to put the oxen away and feed them. Oh – and we have to muck them out.

Pupil 1: Muck them out?

Farm-hand: Yes, clear their dung up and cart it away.

Pupil 1: Oh dear! It sounds a horrible job!

Farm-hand: Yes, but I'm a slave so I have to do what I'm told.

Pupil 2: Shepherd, can you tell us what *you* have to do?

Shepherd: Well, in the early morning I drive the sheep to their pasture. Then I have to stand with my dogs in the wind and rain to keep them safe from greedy wolves. I milk them twice daily, and I use the milk to make butter and cheese.

Hunter: I know how dangerous wolves can be. I go hunting in the forest nearly every day. My dogs chase animals into my nets and I kill them when they're tangled up.

Pupil 3: Can you hunt without nets?

Hunter: Oh yes. My dogs sometimes catch the animals for me.

Pupil 3: What do you kill most often?

Hunter: Stags and bears, roe deer and boars, and sometimes hares.

Pupil 3: Did you go hunting yesterday?

Hunter: Oh yes, I was lucky yesterday. I killed two stags – and a boar as well. Killing the stags was easy because they got caught in my nets. But killing the boar meant risking my life. It was coming towards me and I stood in its way and speared it to death just before it trampled on me.

Pupil 4: What do you do with what you kill?

Hunter: I give the King whatever I kill because I'm his hunter.

Pupil 4: Does the King eat all that meat? Is that why he's fat?

Teacher: Shh! Don't talk in that cheeky way. Hunter, what do you get in return for your work?

Hunter: Food, fine clothes; sometimes a horse or a gold bracelet. I'm lucky to have such a generous master.

Pupil 5: Fisherman, how do you catch your fish?

Fisherman: With my net, my baited hook and my basket. Sometimes I have to stand in the river up to my waist.

Pupil 5: Don't you ever fish in the sea?

Fisherman: Sometimes I do, but not very often. I have to row such a long way to get there. But it gives me a chance to catch big things that earn me a lot of money.

Pupil 5: Like whales, you mean?

Fisherman: Oh no, not whales. They're too powerful for me and my men. And how could I get one into my boat?

Pupil 6: Can the Fowler tell us how he catches birds?

Fowler: Oh in all sorts of way. Sometimes I catch them with snares and traps, sometimes I get them to come by whistling; and sometimes I hunt them down with a hawk.

Pupil 6: A hawk! Do you have to train your hawks?

Fowler: Oh yes, they wouldn't be of any use if I couldn't train them. Now then – I've got a surprise for you all.

Teacher:	Yes, we all want to know what you've got inside that wooden box. There it goes again — it's making some most peculiar noises.
Fowler:	I'll open the lid and I'll show you just how tame a well-trained hawk can be. OW! OUCH!
Teacher:	Are you all right?
Fowler:	Yes, I think it's got a bit frightened, that's all.
Pupil 7:	Can we keep the hawk at school?
Fowler:	I'd swap you a hawk for a fast dog!
Pupil 2:	What do hawks eat?
Pupil 7:	They like bits of finger!
Teacher:	Be sensible! Let the Fowler answer.
Fowler:	In the winter they catch food for themselves and me as well. Then in the spring I let them fly away to the woods. In the autumn I catch a new lot of hawks — young ones — ready to train for the winter.
Pupil 8:	Now let's hear what the shoemaker does.
Shoemaker:	Well, I buy hides and skins and turn them into shoes and all sort of other leather goods. I make bottles and flasks, bridles, straps, purses and bags. You've nothing that lasts the winter unless my skill has gone into it.
Pupil 9:	Salter, how do *you* help us?
Salter:	How do I help you? You'd starve without me. You can't fill your cellar or storehouse unless you have some salt. Butter, meat and vegetables all go bad without salt — so what would you have to eat in the winter?
Teacher:	Monk, you've already told us about yourself, but who do the monks have to help them at the monastery?
Monk:	We have blacksmiths, carpenters and lots of other craftsmen too.
Pupil 8:	Do you have any older monks to advise you?
Monk:	Oh yes, we get a lot of help from older, wiser monks like the Abbot.
Pupil 9:	Can the Abbot tell us which job he thinks is the most important?
Abbot:	Worshipping God is the finest way of spending your life. And farming comes next, because farmers feed us and keep us alive.
Blacksmith:	What rubbish! Where does the ploughman get his share or his coulter? He'd have nothing sharp to plough with if it wasn't for me. Where does the fisherman get his hook or

the cobbler his awl or the tailor his needle? Don't they all depend on me?

Abbot: Well maybe you're right but we'd all prefer to live with the farmer. The farmer gives us food and drink. And what do *you* give us? Sparkling iron, thunderous beating and the puffing of bellows.

Carpenter: What about me? I build your ships – and even your houses. *I'm* the most important of all.

Blacksmith: Carpenter, why do you speak like that when you can't even make a hole without *my* help?

Abbot: Stop arguing. We don't fight in the classroom. But in a way it's right for people to say what they think. It's no good being covered in smiles if your hearts are full of unkind thoughts. Tombs are like that – they're nice on the outside but if you open them up they stink.

Teacher: Our youngest visitor wants to be a monk himself. Perhaps he can tell us what he's done so far today.

Pupil Monk: Oh, I've done all sorts of things. In the night, when I heard the church bell, I got out of bed and went to sing matins with the other monks. It was really cold. I was shivering all through breakfast and prayers. And now I've come to the monastery schoolroom.

Abbot: Have you been caned?

Pupil Monk: No, I've been careful.

Abbot: Tell us what you've eaten today.

Pupil Monk: Only bread. But this evening I shall have some meat. I'm allowed to have meat because I'm a child.

Abbot: What else do you expect to have?

Pupil Monk: Vegetables or beans – and an egg if I'm lucky. And the pupil monks have water from the monastery well. The proper monks have beer with their meals.

Abbot: Well, just a little beer, perhaps. Where do you sleep?

Pupil Monk: We sleep together in the dormitory.

Abbot: Who wakes you up in the night to sing matins?

Pupil Monk: Sometimes we're woken up with a stick. But if we're lucky we hear the bell and get up by ourselves.

Teacher: Ah – there it goes now. It must be time for evening prayers. Where would we be without that bell?

Blacksmith: Which *I* helped to make.

Carpenter: Which *you* couldn't fix in the tower without *me*.

Tony D. Triggs

Children of winter

Setting

A barn in the winter of 1665 and Molly's house.

Characters

Tess; Catherine, her older sister; Dan, their brother; Clem, Dan's friend; Moll, Clem's sister.

Scenery and props

Seventeenth-century costume; a sack; long sticks; a bowl; chairs; a table; food; sound effects for a blizzard, a door closing and so on.

Production notes

It's 1665 and people are dying of the plague. Tess, Catherine and Dan are sent by their parents to a shepherd's barn above the village, in the hope that they will be safe there. Then Clem the shepherd returns....

This drama for nine- to twelve-year-olds was originally written as a play for radio, hence the need for sound effects which the children can devise for themselves. The play can either be performed to an audience or recorded on to tape and presented as the children's own 'radio play'.

Scene 1

(Inside a barn one winter's night.)

Tess: *(Sings creepily.)* When Dan lies asleeping
Asleeping in the night,
Along comes the spider
Up he jumps in fright;
'A ghost' he cries.
'A leggy ghost!
With hairy fingers waving...

(Dan is mock screaming, Catherine is laughing, when there comes a knocking on the door in time to the song. Fade all of this under Catherine's thoughts.)

Catherine: *(Thoughts.)* That night of the singing and dancing in our barn was to be the very last of our merrymaking. Tess had draped a sack over her head and was leaping round with long sticks in her hands so her shadow in the candlelight was spidery and huge, and Dan and I were screeching with laughter, when all of a sudden there came such a banging on our door that our blood nearly froze to our bones.

(Knocking.)

Catherine: Don't open it, Tessa! Don't!

Dan: Yes, do! It'll be the messenger!

Catherine: Dan! *(The door is pulled open. Sound of a blizzard.)*

Clem:	Dan? Is it thee?
Dan:	It's Clem? He's fainted!
Catherine:	Shut the door! I tell thee, shut it! *(She struggles with Dan and closes the door.)*
Dan:	Catherine! 'Tis Clem out there!
Tess:	Bring him in. Tha must!
Catherine:	I daren't bring him in.
Dan:	But Cathy, 'tis Clem. He's my friend.
Catherine:	Tha saw his face. He's sick.
Tess:	Then we must let him in.
Catherine:	Doesn't tha understand?
Dan:	'Tis thee as doesn't understand! It's Clem, and he's sick.
Tess:	Let him in.
Catherine:	Think! Think! If he's sick, then he may have the plague.
Tess:	I understand that. But we can't just leave him there.
Catherine:	What else can we do? What would mother do?
Dan:	Tha knows very well what mother would do. She'd bring him in and give him a good supper, and look after him till he was better, even if she didn't know him.
Catherine:	*(Sighs.)* Very well then. Is the broth still warm?
Tess:	I can soon boil it up. The fire won't be out yet. Shall I do it?
Catherine:	Yes. But... take great care over this. Creep past Clem. Don't go near him. See if tha can build the fire up.

(They open the door. Sounds of blizzard, Clem moaning.)

Dan:	Clem!
Catherine:	Stay here, Dan.
Clem:	I came back here to be alone. I don't know what to do with myself now.
Catherine:	Tha'll be all right, Clem. Dan! Stay with me.
Tess:	The broth is ready.
Catherine:	Bring it in a small bowl, and put it just by him.
Tess:	Here, Clem. Can tha smell it? 'Tis hot, mind, and good for thee.
Clem:	Aye! 'Tis good! God bless thee for this.
Catherine:	Come in now Tessa. We must talk. Leave Clem to finish that. *(They close the door.)*

Tess:	Oh, Catherine!
Catherine:	Let me think.
Dan:	But Cath....
Tess:	Shush Dan. Leave her. 'Tis too hard for thee to understand, this.
Catherine:	I want to help Clem. And yet I must do what Mother wanted, and save us all. Save thee. If we bring Clem in here, and he does have the plague, then we'll catch it too. We may die.
Tess:	We needn't touch him though. He could lie over there, away from us.
Catherine:	But we'd be breathing the air he breathes. I don't know what spreads this plague about from one person to another, but I do know that when he sneezes he puts it into the air. We mustn't even go that close to him, to breathe his air. I won't let thee.
Tess:	So what do we do? We can't leave him out there to die! I think we should risk it and make him better.
Dan:	Catherine, I know what we should do.
Catherine:	Shush Dan.
Tess:	Anyway, how do we know for sure that it is the plague?
Catherine:	Maybe Clem will know. We must talk to him. Clem! Clem! Can tha hear me!
Clem:	*(From the other side of the door.)* Aye, child. I hear thee.
Catherine:	Has tha been down to the village?
Clem:	I have. I went down from the hills just yesterday. I went down to see our Moll.
Catherine:	Did tha see anyone? Did tha see the people at Tebbutt's farm?
Clem:	I saw no one.

Scene 2

(Clem's footsteps are heard in the empty streets.)

Clem:	Doors and shutters closed. No one on the streets. No one in the fields. No voices. Nobody. Nothing. I thought I were sleeping. I've never come on anything like that before. I went on down to our Moll's house, through them quiet streets, and I was cold in the stomach with all this strangeness. *(His footsteps stop.)* Tha knows how noisy our Moll is? Well, there wasn't a sound coming from her house. Moll? Moll? *(Echo.)* And those children of hers. They're like a herd of fresh goats, shouting and leaping and clambering up me as if I was a tree in a field. Not a sign of them! Moll? Where is

everybody? *(Echo.)* I went in thinking to find a feast ready, because there's always plenty of food at Moll's house. Table were set. *(Scrape of chair as he sits himself down.)* They must be gone to market or some such. Well, I'll get tucking in. Why... what's this? Milk's blue in cup. Bread's as stale as stones... *(Moll's voice is heard in upstairs room, crying. Chair is scraped back again.)* Moll? Is that thee? *(He runs upstairs.)* Moll?

Moll: Clem, I wish tha'd never come here.

Clem: Why Moll? What's happened? Where's Peter and all the little ones?

Moll: The little ones are dead.

Clem: What?

Moll: All dead. Dead of the plague. And Peter's outside digging up a place to put them in.

Clem: Molly! Moll.

Moll: Get away from me, Clem. Save thyself at least.

Clem: I can't leave thee like this....

Moll: It's too late for me. Go Clem, save thyself! Go....

Scene 3

(Sounds of blizzard. Clem's voice is heard by children through the door.)

Clem: I knew she was right. I gave her my blessing, and ran for my life out of the village. And now I've started with this fever. Mebbe I can shake it off, I thought, if I can shelter in the barn. How was I to know there'd be three children here already? *(Subsides into coughing.)*

Catherine: *(Whispers.)* It's happened. It's what Mother dreaded above all else. Clem has brought the plague from the village to our barn.

Tess: There's nothing we can do.

Dan: There is! Please listen to me, Catherine. I know what we can do. We can put Clem in the sheep-pen. It's warm and dry in there.

Tess: He's right. We can bring Cloudy and the hens in here. We'll make a stable of the barn, and never mind the smell!

Catherine: And we can light a small fire at the entrance to the sheep pen to keep him warm, and to keep wild animals away.

Dan: And he can have my sack to sleep in.

Berlie Doherty

Sisters

Setting

A bus; the Spencers' living room; a café and a classroom.

Characters

Shelley Makins (aged nine); Ina Spencer (aged nine); Mr Spencer; Mrs Spencer; Beverley Spencer, Ina's sister (aged eighteen); Paul Makins, Shelley's brother (aged eighteen); Mrs Martin, a friend of Mrs Spencer's; Mr Lamb, Shelley and Ina's class teacher; people on the bus and in the café; mounted police officers; children in the classroom.

Scenery and props

Smarties; make-up; mirror; chairs and table; two mugs; desks and chairs; sound effects tape.

Production notes

This play takes place in a pit village in Derbyshire during the 1984 Miners' Strike.

Scene 1

(Shelley Makins and Ina Spencer are kneeling on the bus seats, sucking Smarties. They are facing each other and giggling. Mrs Spencer is talking to an acquaintance, Mrs Martin, on seats just behind the two girls.)

Mrs Spencer: They're so looking forward to being sisters.

(Bus brakes, throwing two girls against each other, making them giggle.)

Mrs Spencer: Sit still, will you!

Mrs Martin: When's the wedding, then?

Mrs Spencer: Ee, I dunno, what with the strike an' all, I dunno. Will you two sit still!

Mrs Martin: *(To Shelley and Ina.)* You going to be bridesmaids, then?

Ina: 'Course we are. Shelley's gonna be in blue and I'm gonna have yellow and our Bev's gonna be all in white and Paul... Paul's....

Shelley: Our Paul'll be in grey but he wain't have one of those top hat things, he says, not even when strike's over, 'cos they're only for posh folks, he says, and....

Ina: Our Bev says he's got no sense and if he hadn't of been on strike he could of hired the lot at one of those special shops, she says. She says Paul's dad ought to know better than....

Mrs Spencer: Now, c'mon, don't you two start arguing. And never you mind what our Bev says about Paul's dad. It's got nowt to do with her. And sit round straight!

(Shelley and Ina glare at each other.)

Shelley: Our Paul says your dad's a blackleg and he's making money when he didn't ought to be, and our Paul's had to sell his bike and you all went to Skeggy and we didn't get to go to Skeggy, did we? So there!

Mrs Martin: Now then, that's no way to talk to someone who's going to be your sister.

Shelley: Don't care! Don't want her to be my sister, don't want her silly sister to marry our Paul, so there! An' I wain't give you any more of my Smarties!

Ina: Don't want any more of your smelly old Smarties!

(Bus comes to a halt. Mrs Spencer gets up.)

Mrs Spencer: Come on, you two. *(To Mrs Martin.)* Ta-ra.

Mrs Martin: Hope things'll sort out for you all.

Mrs Spencer: Aye, happen they will, one way or another. And that's the last time I take you two shopping. Leastways, till you mend your manners. So think on.

(Mrs Spencer and girls get off bus, both girls keeping away from each other.)

Scene 2

(Ina has been surreptitiously trying out Beverley's make-up and she now has a face like a clown. She is admiring herself in the mirror.)

Mr Spencer: *(Voice from the hall.)* Ina, Ina, where are you?

Ina: What you want, Dad?

(Ina makes half-hearted attempt to remove make-up and stands with her back to the door. Mr Spencer comes in.)

Ina: Yes, Dad?

Mr Spencer: Now listen my lass. *(Ina turns round.)* Eee, whatever have you been up to? Go and get yoursen cleaned up. No, wait on, till I've told you what, first. You are not playing with that Shelley Makins again. D'you hear?

Ina: But me an' Shelley are gonna be sisters. *(She starts to cry.)*

Mr Spencer: Now, shut that noise!

(Beverley walks into living room, having just returned from work.)

Beverley: What on earth've you been up to? You been at my make-up, haven't you? Tell her, Dad. Go on, Dad, tell her!

Ina: Bev, you're gonna marry Paul, aren't you?

Beverley:	'Course I'm gonna marry Paul, but what's that got to do with you messing around with my make-up?
Mr Spencer:	Not so fast, my lass. Nowt's settled yet, as can't be put right. I'm never having a daughter of mine married to a man who calls me a blackleg, so think on!
Beverley:	Eh, Dad, what are you on about?
Ina:	I wanna be Shelley's sister.
Beverley:	Ooh, shut up, our Ina, I wanna be Paul's wife. What are you on about, Dad?
Mr Spencer:	You know very well what I'm on about. Now shut it, I'm watching telly.
Beverley:	Dad!
Ina:	Dad!
Mrs Spencer:	*(Coming into living room.)* Now you two, come out into the kitchen for a minute and help me, will you? And leave your Dad alone.

(The two girls follow their mother out of the room while Dad sits down to watch television.)

Scene 3

(Beverley sits waiting at a table in a café. Paul enters.)

Paul:	Hey-up, Bev.
Beverley:	Paul.
Paul:	Eh, what's up? You look really bad. Has your dad been on to you again?
Beverley:	It's worse than ever, Paul. He says I haven't to marry you 'cos of strike. 'Cos you're on one side, sort of thing, and we're on t'other. My dad says you've been calling him behind his back like an' he won't have it. An' I dunno what our Ina's been up to and your Shelley but they're making it worse.
Paul:	D'you want summat to drink?
Beverley:	Oh, Paul.
Paul:	Jus' a minute. I'll get us two coffees. Don't cry, we'll sort it somehow, Bev. *(Gets up and comes back with two mugs.)* There you go.
Beverley:	Oh, ta.
Paul:	Y'know, I an't said owt about your dad that's not true.
Beverley:	Well, I dunno if you have or you han't, but summat's all wrong, Paul. Blow the strike!
Paul:	Aye, but we can't blow it.

Beverley: Wish the whole thing wa' over.

Paul: But it isn't, Bev, it isn't and we've gorra live through it. I can't walk out on me dad. Nor on me mum, come to that. And anyroad, we're right to be on strike.

Beverley: Well, an' who says I can walk out on my dad, eh? An' I don't think strike's gonna get you lot anywhere. My dad says it's all wrong, doesn't he?

Paul: Oh, Bev, don't let's go through all that again. You know right well what I think about it, y'know – well, y'know, don't you?

Beverley: No, I don't know. All I know is that this strike – why can't you come out of it, why can't you come out of it?

Paul: How can I? I'm surprised you wanna ask me to. I thought you'd have more respect for me than that, Bev, for what I believe in, for what's right.

Beverley: An' what about what I believe's right?

Paul: You don't believe anything, you're just following your dad, that's what you're doing!

Beverley: And you're not following your dad, eh Paul? Well?

Paul: Oh Bev!

Beverley: I mean it. I mean, just 'cos your mum's on that committee an' everything, you think you're all so... so... well, you're not, Paul, and I don't wanna marry you and I don't want anything more to do with you. *(Flounces out leaving Paul bewildered.)*

Scene 4

(The children are lining up outside the classroom, quarrelling about who's in front. Silence as Shelley and Ina and their class file in.)

Shelley: *(In a whisper.)* Ina! Ina!

Mr Lamb: Be quiet.

Shelley: Ina!

Mr Lamb:	I am still waiting for quiet. Come here, Michelle Makins.
Shelley:	Please sir, it wasn't me, it was Ina, sir.
Mr Lamb:	I said, come here, Michelle Makins.
Shelley:	Yes, sir. *(Shelley approaches Mr Lamb's desk. Ina smiles gleefully.)*
Mr Lamb:	Michelle Makins, you are no longer an infant, you have not been an infant for the best part of a year. It is time you knew that when I say be quiet, I mean be quiet.
Shelley:	Yes, sir.
Mr Lamb:	Sit down.
Shelley:	Yes, sir.
Mr Lamb:	Right, open your history books on page 33. Copy out the bit opposite the picture which shows children working down the mines. Remember we looked at it yesterday.

(Children start copying. Eventually silence is broken by sound of pit hooter. The children ignore it. The sound of horses' hooves is heard. The children look up and all stop writing.)

Ina:	Look, the police with their horses!
Shelley:	They must be going down to the pit.

(Children jump up on desks craning to see out of windows.)

Children:	I can't see. Move over, will you. There's hundreds of them. All them horses. What are they gonna do?
Mr Lamb:	Will you sit down! At once! Will you sit DOWN!
Shelley:	My dad's down there with the pickets. What are the horses gonna do, do you think?
Ina:	My dad'll be there too going into work.
Shelley:	Oh, Ina, I'm really frightened.
Ina:	'S all right, Shelley, your dad'll be all right.

(Shelley helps Ina down. Gradually all children sit down.)

Mr Lamb:	There's nowt to worry about. Just get on with your history.
Ina:	*(In a whisper.)* We will stay friends, won't we Shelley?
Shelley:	'Course we will.

Liz Cashdan

OUR WORLD

Improvisations

The first three of the following improvisations are suitable for use with younger age groups while the last one is more appropriate for junior pupils and those who have developed reading fluency. The class could be divided into groups and given one of the situations to improvise. Possible ideas and suggestions are given in italics.

Robots

Setting

Anywhere.

Characters

A variety of robots.

Scenery and props

A piece of music with a rhythmic beat, such as 'In the Air Tonight' by Phil Collins.

Production notes

This improvisation can work successfully with any age group but five- to six-year-olds especially love it. First, discuss any robots, puppets, clockwork toys and so on, that the children have seen, concentrating on the way they move. Help them to become aware of the relative inflexibility of joints, slower reactions due to hydraulics, stopping one action before beginning the next and so on.

Let the children practise moving like robots, encouraging them to let themselves be helped by the beat of the music. Progress from walking to stretching, turning, bending and other movements. Then, put them into pairs and discuss what robots could do as a pair *(production line, tennis, dancing, football, sawing with a two-handled saw)*. Encourage as wide a variety of ideas as possible. Let them practise their chosen activity for a couple of playings of the music. If any are particularly good they can be performed in front of the class. This is a good way to round off the activity.

Heather Cawte Winskill

The pet

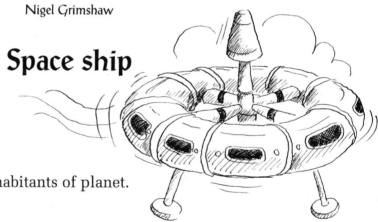

Setting

A residential area.

Characters

A man; his neighbours; his family; other characters as appropriate.

Production notes

This improvisation introduces the concept of the responsibilities of pet-ownership and is suitable for use with seven- to eight-year-olds. The children should be encouraged to decide for themselves what characters they wish to introduce into the improvisation.

A man buys an unusual pet which might be dangerous like a lion cub, or noisy like a howler monkey. His neighbours are unhappy about this and discuss their problem. They call on the man to complain. His family join in the argument. Are they all on his side or do some of them also dislike or fear the animal? Does the man listen to their complaints or does he get angry? Does someone call in the police? Does the animal escape? Act out what happens.

Nigel Grimshaw

Space ship

Setting

A space ship.

Characters

Settlers; crew; Captain; inhabitants of planet.

Production notes

This dramatic improvisation can be used with nine- to twelve-year-olds. Before the activity, ask the children to arrange chairs and tables to represent the inside of a space ship.

The space ship is taking settlers to another planet. Most of the participants are settlers, but there are also crew and a Captain of the ship. They talk about what is being left behind and speculate on what is to come. Some crises can be introduced: for example, a power failure in the craft; a collision with space debris; an attack by alien entities.

Eventually the ship lands on the new planet and the settlers meet the curious inhabitants. The drama could end at the point of arrival.

Charles Thomson

The new invention

Setting

The Emperor's palace, China, 200 BC.

Characters

Inventors; the Emperor; guards; courtiers.

Scenery and props

A cleared space; a throne for the Emperor.

Production notes

This improvisation for older children can involve the whole class. Children's design and technology skills can be tested in devising inventions. They could work them out on paper beforehand.

The inventors have been queuing for hours to meet the Emperor and show him their inventions. It has been a hot and tiring day. They have had a long journey to get to the Emperor, and his bossy guards give the inventors a hard time. The guards think all inventors are mad.

The inventions could be anything which we find useful today, but would have to be made out of bamboo, paper or silk, animal skins, stone, pottery or metals – plastic didn't exist. The inventions could be almost anything from a new kitchen device to a glider.

The inventors practise demonstrating their inventions. They know that if they don't impress the Emperor, they might end up in a dungeon – or worse! A good invention will be well rewarded.

The Emperor is a spoilt and proud person who is on the look out for inventions which will either increase his power, such as weapons, or which are so miraculous that he can claim credit for them. He is as disdainful of his inventors as he possibly can be, even if he is impressed.

The guards follow the Emperor's orders. They are very contemptuous of these inventors, and take pleasure in leading those who have been insufficiently impressive off to the dungeons. The inventors who do well are rewarded by the guards with bags of money.

The inventors themselves can applaud and get excited about the things their fellow scientists have devised. To the disdain of both the Emperor and the guards, they should demonstrate their lack of restraint.

The courtiers could be the Emperor's supporters or they may be genuinely concerned about governing China in a sensible way. Perhaps some of the inventions – cannons, flying machines, paper money – are threatening to their interests. Perhaps some of them – knives and forks, for example – might be a threat to the traditional Chinese way of life. The courtiers might get together and discuss the possible effects, or else protest outright to the Emperor to stop the parade of inventions.

Perhaps something is invented which changes everything for good. What it it? What happens?

Nick Pollard

Dramatic poems and dialogues

The caterpillar

Production notes

This poem can be used as a mime activity with five- to six-year-olds. Before reading the poem, talk about how caterpillars and butterflies move to give pupils ideas for how they themselves should move.

Curled up on a leaf,
Shined on by the sun,
The tiny little egg
Doesn't jump or run.
Then the egg cracks open.
What can be inside?
The hungry caterpillar
Doesn't want to hide.
It crawls into the sunshine
Nibbling as it goes,
Crawling up a bean stalk,
Crawling down a rose.
Then it makes a cosy home.

The time is getting late.
What is going to happen?
We will have to wait.
When the front door opens,
We see a change has come
about.
Not a caterpillar, but a
Butterfly comes out.

(As you read this poem, children should move in ways they feel are appropriate to mime the action suggested by the words.)

Carol Ann Piggins

The clock

Production notes

This short poem can be used as a mime exercise for very young children with the teacher reading the poem and the children performing the actions indicated in italics.

Wind the clock, wind the clock.
(The children mime winding a clock.)
Tick-tock, tick-tock.
(The children swing their arms like a pendulum.)
Listen for the chime.
(The children cup their hands to their ears.)
Bong! Bong! Bong! Bong!
(The children mime hammering a bell.)

Carol Ann Piggins

Opposites

Characters

Mimes are suggested for various characters – other words can be added to give further speaking and miming parts.

Production notes

The children hold hands in two circles which represent opposites. The circles turn slowly and as they turn, a child from each circle comes forward to act out a simple mime. As they finish their mimes the children join hands to form a third group, so that at the end all the children are in one large group.

When the children are in one large group they join hands and dance in a circle. The teacher might organise a team game to finish the session.

All: Come and join us.

(The circles start turning.)

Fast: *(Running quickly.)* I am fast.

Slow: *(Trudging slowly.)* I am slow.

High: *(Stretching.)* I am high.

Low: *(Crouching.)* I am low.

Young: *(Crawling.)* I am young.

Old: *(Walking slowly and bent over.)* I am old.

Hot: *(Wiping forehead.)* I am hot.

Cold: *(Shivering.)* I am cold.

Happy: *(Smiling.)* I am happy.

Sad: *(Crying.)* I am sad.

Good: *(One child helps the other to walk.)* I am good.

Bad: *(Poking out tongue.)* I am bad.

All: Opposites attract.

(The children dance in a circle.)

Alan Brown

The turning year

Characters

As written, this play has twenty-four parts. However, by doubling up on speaking parts or using other voices for the 'All' parts, the numbers can be decreased or increased.

Production notes

This piece can be performed as a circular dance.

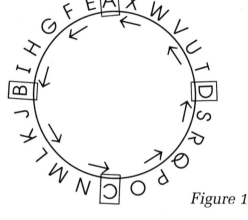

(The children stand in a circle as shown in Figure 1.)

All: The year is turning
           The year is turning
           The year is turning
           every day.

(As they speak the children circle round.)

A: From autumn

B: Into winter

C: Into spring

D: Into summer.

Figure 1

(Each speaker moves into the centre of the circle and then back again, in turn, as they speak.)

All: The year is turning
           every day.

(As they speak the children circle round.)

A: Autumn

E: The leaves turn brown

F: Fall down

G: make a tablecloth

H: crackling

I: on the ground.

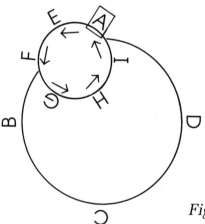

Figure 2

(This group of children form a separate circle and circle round as they speak. They then return to the main group.)

All: The year is turning
           every day.

(As they speak the children circle round.)

B: Winter

J: The ground turns white

K: At night

L: Makes a mirror

M: shining

N: in the light.

(This group of children form a separate circle and circle round as they speak. They then return to the main group.)

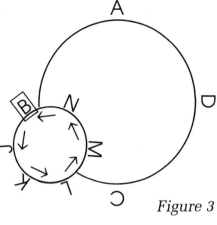

Figure 3

All: The year is turning
every day.

(As they speak the children circle round.)

C: Spring

O: The trees turn green

P: and clean

Q: make a picture

R: The best

S: I've ever seen.

(This group of children form a separate circle and circle round as they speak. They then return to the main group.)

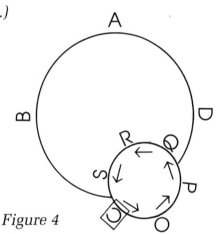

Figure 4

All: The year is turning
every day.

(As they speak the children circle round.)

D: Summer

T: The ground turns hot

U: And what

V: Makes me happy?

W: Ice cream

X: Give me a lot!

(This group of children form a separate circle and circle round as they speak. They then return to the main group.)

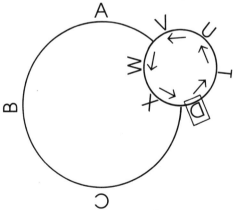

Figure 5

All: The year is turning
every day.

(As they speak the children circle round.)

Ian McMillan

The Nameless Nothing from Nowhere

Setting

A wood.

Characters

Trees; the Nameless Nothing; Wind; Water; Chorus; Crocodile; Snake; Ants; Sergeant-Major Ant; Caterpillar; Tortoise.

Production notes

This piece examines the natural world and the interrelationships of the various things within it, including the 'Nameless Nothing', humankind. It can be performed by the whole class and is suitable for juniors.

(Several Trees stand, backs to the audience. They sway as several Wind figures push and pull at them, slowly, without touching. The Nameless Nothing enters and stops.)

Nameless Nothing: Where am I? It's dark in this forest. I can't see. What's that noise?

(One Wind steps forward.)

Wind: Bustling and jostling and rustling and shuffling....
The wood's in my way, the wood's in my way.
Huffing and hustling and tussling and muscling....
The wood's in my way, the wood's in my way....

Nameless Nothing: I know who you are. You're the Wind.

Wind: That's me.

(Wind steps back into the 'forest'. Water creeps forwards.)

Water: Lick – lap – slip – slap
dip – duck – can't keep up
with the slip and the slap and the slither of me
with the drip and the splash and the glitter of me
on the slide you can't stop to the sea, to the sea....

Nameless Nothing: I know who you are. You're Water.

Water: That's me.

(Water trickles back into the forest. Nameless Nothing steps back and bumps into Tree.)

Tree: Sticks and stones – and finger bones
witches' hair – head in the air
catch at your clothes – trip your toes
    owl hooting WHO? WHO? WHO?

Nameless Nothing: I know who you are. You're a Tree.

Tree: That's me.

Nameless Nothing: If you're the Water, you're the Tree,
you're the Wind... WHO CAN I BE?

Wind: You're Nameless.

Water: You're Nothing.

Tree: You come from Nowhere.

Wind/Water/Tree: You're a Nameless Nothing from Nowhere.

Nameless Nothing: But I only want to know!

Wind/Water/Tree: *(Echoes.)* ...no   ...no   ...no ....

Nameless Nothing: They're not going to help me. What can I do?

Chorus: *Move along now, move along.*

(The 'forest' steps back. Nameless Nothing trudges on.)

Chorus: Dead leaves crunching at my feet....
Move along now, move along.
Never know who you might meet....
Move along now, move along.

(Nameless Nothing stops suddenly, Water moves aside to reveal Crocodile lying in wait.)

Crocodile: One eye above the mud... waiting...
a back like bark – hardly breaking the surface.

Nameless Nothing: Who are you?

Crocodile: I'm the contemplating Crocodile calculating
    carefully....
A fat frog foolishly flopping? Not today.
A sleepy sloth slipping from his branch? Not today.
A snack between meals spoils your appetite, they
    say.
But NOTHING spoils my appetite....

Nameless Nothing: I'm Nothing. That's what everybody says.

Crocodile: Oh no, you're not. You're just like me. I've seen you
snatch, snap and gobble things whole and all the
time you're doing it you smile, like me. I know you.
You're a crocodile!

Nameless Nothing: No. No. It isn't true.
I haven't got scaly skin or tombstone teeth
or a whiplash tail. I'm not like you.
I'm a Nameless Nothing from Nowhere
and I only want to know!
If I'm not a crocodile, then WHO?

Chorus: *(Repeat.) Move along now, move along....*

(Nameless Nothing trudges on, then stops, suddenly aware of Snake wrapped round a tree.)

Snake:	Light and shade, – Sun and shadow coiling till – the patterns ripple nightshade flowing – Sun dapple....
Nameless Nothing:	Who are you?
Snake:	*(Moving very close.)* I'm *sss*o *s*sorry. I *sss*ee it in your eyes. *S*sit down. Tell me your *s*story. Let me *s*sympathise.... I too have my *s*secret *s*sorrow. There's nothing you can't share with me.
Nameless Nothing:	But *I'm* Nothing! That's what they say.
Snake:	Oh but you *are s*something! I've seen you all *s*sympathy... all *s*sugary... when your friend is *s*sad, *s*squeezing the good times for a drop of bad. I can *s*see what you are. You're a *s*snake like me.
Nameless Nothing:	No, no, I'm not like you! I haven't got a tongue that forks and flicks. I'm not a snake, but WHO?
Chorus:	*(Repeat.) Move along now, move along....*

(Nameless Nothing trudges on. All 'insect' figures can mime their creatures with their hands. Looks down as Ants march out of the forest.)

Nameless Nothing:	And who are YOU?
Sergeant-Major Ant:	Left! Right! Left! Right! Left! Right! No, left! I mean, right! That's right, left! No....
Nameless Nothing:	*(Notices Caterpillar in forest.)* And who are YOU?
Caterpillar:	Mmmm. Munch. Crunch. Yum. Burp. Yawn. Sigh.
Nameless Nothing:	Who are you all?
Sergeant-Major Ant:	Ant patrol, atten-shun! Right, lads! Get yer legs in order. One. Two. One. Two. No, Three. Four. Five. Six. Pull yerself together. You 'orrible little ant. Who do you think you are? Ant patrol... march! Nothing gets in our way.
Caterpillar:	*(Yawns.)* Just take it easy. There's nowhere to go. Just go to eat. Wait and see how you grow. I could change into... anything, just wait and see. Why, I could be... a dragonfly? a dragon! a rhinoceros!! anything!!! Nothing's out of the question for me.
Nameless Nothing:	But *I'm* Nothing. I'm not any of you. I can be a bit bossy.... But I'm not a soldier ant. Sometimes I daydream when I should be out and doing but I'm not a caterpillar.
All:	But you must be something!
Nameless Nothing:	I'm a Nameless Nothing from Nowhere and I *still* want to know!

All:	*(Closing in.)* Come on now, you've got to choose. Choose! Choose!
Nameless Nothing:	No! No! No! Too much noise. Leave me alone!

(Other characters shuffle off, leaving Tortoise, disguised as a boulder.)

Nameless Nothing:	They've gone. I'm on my own. There's nothing left but one – grey – stone. I'll sit down and think.
Tortoise:	O-o-oy.... What's going on? O-o-oy.... That's my back you're sitting on.
Nameless Nothing:	*(Jumps up.)* I'm sorry. Who are you?

Tortoise:	I'm a Terribly Ancient Tortoise and I've seen it all before. I'm too old to hurry or scurry or worry. I've seen it all before all this grabbing and grousing and gobbling and gabbing and chopping and changing and whinging and whining and lefting and righting and picking and choosing and contemplating – calculating wanting waiting – loving hating... If you want someone with *experience*, I'm the one. There's nothing new under the Sun.
Nameless Nothing:	But what am I? Please tell me.
Tortoise:	Aren't you one of those running-around-and-asking-questions things, one of those grabbing-and-grousing-and-gobbling-and-gabbling things, one of those....
Nameless Nothing:	WHO?
Tortoise:	Hu–man being.
Nameless Nothing:	A *human being?*
Tortoise:	Just like all the others.
Nameless Nothing:	What, you mean I'm not the only one?
Tortoise:	The only one?! There are *billions* of you out there.

(Nameless Nothing looks up at the audience, as if seeing them for the first time. The rest of the cast come on stage, moving in their different ways. As tortoise speaks, they move towards the audience, staring and pointing.)

Take a look. See? All those people, watching, listening. Who do they think they are? Go on, ask them WHO!

Helen Dunmore and Philip Gross

Developments

Setting

A street.

Characters

Two friends.

Production notes

This dialogue is suitable for nine- to twelve-year-olds.

Y: It's ages since we walked up this road.

Z: Hasn't it changed!

Y: There used to be an old house here.

Z: The garden was all overgrown.

Y: The garden wall's still there.

Z: And that tree – look – in front of it.

Y: But there's not much else.
What do you think they're doing?

Z: All they've done so far
is turn it into a load of mud.

Y: It says 'Construction'.

Z: Building houses, I suppose.

Y: They've already built some here.

Z: Horrible, aren't they.

Y: My friend used to live round here....
It *was* here!
It was where these new ones are –
they must have pulled it down.

Z: I suppose so.

Y: It was a brilliant house.
It had a sort of tower
with ivy all over the walls.

Z: It sounds really creepy.

Y: It was.

Z: I thought they couldn't pull down
old houses like that.

Y: Well, they must have –
it's not there now, is it?

Z: No. Nor are the allotments.
Look over there.

Y: There's a whole new road!
We used to play over the allotments.

Z: They don't hang about, do they?

Y: That old guy used to chase us away.
The one with the walking stick
and a funny nose.

Z: 'Get off my lettuce, at once!'

Y: I wonder if he chased away
the cement mixers.

Z: Probably died of a heart attack.

Y: There's more buildings up this end as well.

Z: The football pitch was here
and a church on the other side.

Y: No, hang on –
it was the church here.

Y: No, it was the football pitch.

Z: No, I've got it.
Look –
they've changed the direction of the road.
It goes right through
where the football pitch used to be,
and that warehouse....

Y: ...is where the church was.
They've changed it all.

Z: I liked it how it was.

Y: Yes, it was all right,
but people have got to have somewhere to live.

Y: Well, there's nowhere else round here
left to build on, is there?

Z: There's the river.

Y: Don't be daft.

Z: Haven't you heard?
They've got a plan
to put a concrete roof over the river
and build a shopping centre on it.

Y: Very funny....
You are joking,
aren't you?

Charles Thomson

Acceleration gravytrain rap

Characters

Two groups of speakers, one low voiced to say the food phrases and one clear and higher to be the train verses.

Production notes

This rap is spoken by two groups simultaneously. The higher voiced group speak the train verses in 4/4 time (except the last verse which is spoken in 2/2 time) while the lower voiced group repeat the food phrases.

Aim to build up energy and pace after a slow quiet start to imitate the acceleration of the train. At LOCO LOCO the steady rhythm is spoken over 'barbecue' said quickly, until both groups shout on 'wheee!' and make a long whisper on 'gone.......'.

Soft hand claps with cupped hands can add percussion effect and emphasise the rhythms.

♫♫♩ ♩/♫♫♩

locomotive engine	*peanut butter biscuits*
locomotive track	*peanut butter biscuits*
locomotive riders	*peanut butter biscuits*
all the way and back.	*peanut butter biscuits*

♫♫♩♩ ♩/♫♫♩♩ ♩/

loco-locomotive	*pepperoni pizza*
taking no heed	*pepperoni pizza*
loco-locomotive	*pepperoni pizza*
picking up speed.	*pepperoni pizza*

♪♩ ♪♩ ♩/♪♩ ♪♩ ♩/

loco-mo-motive	*sausage and baked beans*
hedges whipping by	*sausage and baked beans*
loco-mo-motive	*sausage and baked beans*
'mazing how we fly.	*sausage and baked beans*

♪♩ ♫♩♩/♪♩ ♫♩♩/

loco-mo-mo-t-tive	*French fried piranha fish*
rat-tat on rails	*French fried piranha fish*
loco-mo-mo-t-tive	*French fried piranha fish*
tunnel hills and dales.	*French fried piranha fish*

♩ ♩ / ♩ ♩ /

LOCO LOCO LOCO LOCO	*barbecue, barbecue, barbecue, barbecue*
LOCO loco LOCO loco	*barbecue, barbecue, barbecue, barbecue*
loco loco	*barbecue, barbecue*
wheee!.....	*wheee!*
gone.......!	*gone......!*

Maggie Norton

Scripted drama

Time to make friends

Setting

A family home and outside in the street.

Characters

Twelve children (chorus of narrators); Dad; Mum; Flea; Second (a puppy); Spotty-Dog-Posh; Cassandra (Spotty-Dog-Posh's silent partner).

Scenery and props

A loofah; an aerosol can; a shampoo bottle; a torch.

Production notes

This play, written in rhyme, can be used with seven- to eight-year-olds.

Scene 1

(A family home.)

Narrators:	Second was orphaned, arrived in a box – a puppy so ugly was rather a shock but Second's new family engulfed him with hugs and Second responded by sharing his bugs....
Dad:	This animal, dear, is infested with fleas!
Mum:	Better, I think, than some dreaded disease.
Narrators:	Comforted Mum as she scratched at her arm.
Mum:	Fleas can be dealt with. We'll come to no harm. Fleas can be captured. We'll catch them with ease.
Dad:	Just make it quick then, my dear, if you please.
Narrators:	Squirmed Dad with a loofah brush pushed up his shirt.
Dad:	Scrubbing with loofahs, when dry, sure does hurt.
Narrators:	Dogs that have lodgers can soon lose their charm.
Mum:	Combatting pests is no problem. Keep calm.
Narrators:	So out came the aerosol – '*PRESS IT AND SQUIRT*' and Second retreated to hide up Mum's skirt but later lay squinting towards his nose end: deep in his freckles was tickling a 'friend' that suddenly sank in its tongue for a drink of dog's-blood. *OF DOG'S-BLOOD!* No pause for a think –

	Second raised his... *(Raises leg.)* then let it descend!
Flea:	I'd better play possum.
Narrators:	Said Flea.
Flea:	I'll pretend to die and I'll lie with my legs keeping still for batting-by-paws can make one feel ill but any old mongrel must know to its cost that drowning's the only way fleas can be lost.
Dad:	These pests, they are proving too hard to arrest. Let's give him a bath. That's what I suggest.
Narrators:	Said Dad as if reading the brain of a flea was something he did quite regularly. So Second was stripped of his collar, and bare was plonked in the bath where they wetted his hair and shampoo'd his body with *GLOSENE.*
Second:	It's green!
Narrators:	Thought Second.
Second:	A colour on which I'm not keen. What if it dyes me? I'll die! Can't be seen trotting around like some Cruft's Beauty Queen.
Narrators:	Decided, determined, you know what I mean, he doggedly stated....
Second:	Don't want to be clean!
Narrators:	By fleeing the bath in a rainbow-ish blur and shaking the wet up the walls to deter his new foster family from doggone pursuing, Second knew naturally what he was doing. There seemed little reason for having a wash – but that was before he met *Spotty-Dog-Posh.*

Scene 2

(Outside in the street.)

Spotty-Dog-Posh:	How terribly undognified.
Narrators:	Sneered Spott, the local snob, as trotting up the street he spied a green fluorescent... dog?
Spotty-Dog-Posh:	An accident like that....
Narrators:	Spott sighed.
Spotty-Dog-Posh:	Could cost a breeder's job. What formula for *that* applied? Half pig? Half dog? A *POG?* Come, Come Cassandra, come away,

	with that we'll not acquaint. For pedigrees one's people pay.
Narrators:	That's one thing Second ain't!
Spotty-Dog-Posh:	Come, come Cassandra, come away. Sweetspot, you mustn't faint. The air here has, one's bound to say, a rather nasty taint.
Second:	I'll knock your spots off. Black your eyes and punch your snooty nose. No decent dog would be disguised as reject dominoes!

(A clock strikes midnight as Narrators stand in a clock-face formation with Second at the centre.)

Narrators:	Retorted Second feeling hurt, abandoned and alone and curling in the dust and dirt sobbed for his proper home...
	but as each stroke of midnight sounds black figures take their place till twelve true friends have gathered round one Second's shining face.

(Beam of torch shines on face like second hand of clock.)

Gina Douthwaite

Prize surprise

Setting

The Joneses' kitchen and a field near a power station.

Characters

Mr Jones; Mrs Jones; Billy Jones, their son; Mr Strong; Janice, Mr Strong's assistant; two television camera crew; a crowd of onlookers, some with speaking parts.

Scenery and props

A table; chairs; a letter; some fencing; outdoor clothes; detonator box (this can be made from a cardboard box); earphones; clipboard; camcorder; sound effects tape.

Production notes

This drama for seven- to eight-year-olds can involve the whole class. The children can be encouraged to devise and record their own sound effects.

Scene 1

(The kitchen of an ordinary house. The Jones family, Mum, Dad and Billy, are having breakfast. A letter is heard dropping through the letter-box.)

Mum:	That was the postman.
Billy:	I'll go! *(He runs off and comes back with a letter.)*
Billy:	It's for you, Dad! *(Hands letter over.)*
Dad:	I wonder what this is? I wasn't expecting any letters.
Mum:	Well, go on! Open it!
Dad:	*(Opens letter and gasps.)* Wow! You'll never guess what! I entered a competition a while ago for the whole family, and we've won a prize.
Billy:	Hey, great!
Mum:	A prize! Well, that makes a nice change from all the bills. What have we won?
Dad:	*(Becoming mysterious.)* Ah! Now that's a secret. You'll just have to wait and see.
Billy:	Oh, come on, Dad! Tell us what it is. *(Peeps over Dad's shoulder to try to see what's in the letter, but Dad snatches it away.)*
Dad:	No, I you'll just have to keep guessing until Saturday.
Billy:	*(Groans.)* We can't wait that long! Saturday's ages off!
Mum:	Now, Dad, I don't see why you can't tell us. You said it was for all the family. You're just going to get our Billy all upset.

Dad: Well, it's time our Billy learned a bit of patience. Anyway, it will be something special to look forward to. *(He gets up from the table.)* I'd better be off now. I've got to go and fix up about this prize on my way to work. *(Exit.)*

Mum: Well, I never!

Billy: It's not fair. Dad could have told us what the prize was.

Mum: I expect it's nothing much, or he *would* have told us.

Billy: If it's for the family it might be a new car.

Mum: No such luck!

Billy: Or a new house.

Mum: Go on with you!

Billy: Or a holiday to Disneyland!

Mum: The very idea!

Billy: Hey, what if it's free chocolate for life?

Scene 2

(A field with a fenced-off bit at one end. Inside the fence is a strange box with a T-shaped handle on top. It is now Saturday and Mum, Dad and Billy are walking across the field on the way to get their prize. Mum stops for a rest so the others stop too.)

Mum: *(Grumbling.)* What a way to spend a Saturday morning! It's cold out here – *and* muddy. Just look at my shoes!

Dad: Well, I told you to put your wellies on, didn't I?

Mum: You can't be presented with a prize in your wellies. Whatever would people think?

Billy: I've got mine on!

Dad: Sensible lad! Anyway, it's not far now.

Mum: What do you mean, it's not far? Whoever heard of a prize being presented in a field?

Billy: *(Pointing ahead to somewhere off-stage.)* Hey look, that's the power station over there!

Dad: That's right! I told you we were nearly there.

Billy: Have we won the power station, Dad?

Dad: Not exactly!

(A crowd gathers from the direction of the power station. People stroll along, dressed in outdoor clothes and chatting excitedly.)

Mum: What's going on,? What are all these people doing here?

Billy: Have they come to see us get our prize?

(Mr Strong appears, wearing earphones, and walks towards Dad. Mr Strong's assistant, Janice, is with him. Janice is carrying a clipboard.)

Mr Strong: *(Shaking hands with Dad.)* Good! You made it, then, Mr Jones. *(Turns to Janice.)* Janice, these are our lucky prize winners.

Janice: Pleased to meet you all! *(She turns to Billy.)* You must be Billy. You must be very excited about what's going to happen.

Billy: I don't *KNOW* what's going to happen. Dad won't tell us.

Dad: *(Glancing uneasily at Mum.)* I thought it would be better as a surprise in case anybody got scared.

Mum: Scared?

Mr Strong: Oh, there's nothing to be scared about. It's all absolutely safe, as long as everybody keeps out of the danger zone.

Mum: *(In alarm.)* What danger zone?

Mr Strong: Oh, that's a good distance away, Mrs Jones. You'll be fine because Janice is here to look after you. She'll tell you exactly where to stand.

Janice: Yes, and I think we'd better go and get into place now. It's nearly time. Just follow me, please. *(She starts off towards the fence and the box, and the Jones family follow.)*

Janice: Now, if you'll just stand round the box, like this... *(She places Mum, Dad and Billy behind the box.)*

Mum: I wish I knew what was going on.

Dad: *(Sounding important.)* We're going to blow up the power station.

Billy: Blow it up? Whatever for?

Janice: The power station is too old now to be of any use, so we are going to pull it down, then something else can be built on the site. Maybe a new school, or a swimming-pool or a giant toy-shop; you never know your luck!

Billy: You mean, Mum and Dad and me are going to blow it up?

Janice: That's right! When Mr Strong gives the signal to me I'll say *PRESS!* And you must all three press down hard on this handle. Here, Billy, you'd better stand in the middle.

(Janice rearranges the Jones family while Mr Strong organises the crowd.)

Mr Strong: Now then, ladies and gentlemen, if you'd just stand clear, please.... This way, madam! Could you just move back a bit, sir?

Woman: Hey, I can't see now!

Man: There's nothing to see yet.

Woman:	Well, I want a good view for when there is.
Crowd:	Ssssh!
Mr Strong:	Well, ladies and gentlemen, you all know what's about to happen. At exactly eleven o'clock we hope to blow up the power station. It should be a spectacular sight, something for you all to remember for the rest of your lives. But I must ask you please to keep well behind the red tape.
Billy:	Hey, isn't this exciting, Mum?
Mum:	Yes, I suppose it is. It's not every day you get to blow up a power station.
Janice:	Best of all, it's going to be filmed for television. See, here come the camera crew now. *(Enter two camera crew who take up positions near the Jones family.)*
Mr Strong:	Now, I think we're almost ready. Let's have a countdown of ten. Quiet please, everyone! *(He begins to count.)* Ten – nine – eight – seven – six – five – four – three – two – one – zero!
Janice:	Now – press!

(Mum, Dad and Billy press down on the T-shaped handle. There is a great boom off stage and all the crowd gasps, then cheers.)

Woman:	Look at that!
Man:	What a sight!
Woman:	I never saw anything like it!
Man:	Came down like a house of cards!
Woman:	*(Coughing.)* Hasn't half made a dust, though!
Janice:	Well done! That went off beautifully.
Mr Strong:	Couldn't have done it better myself! Well, young Billy, did you enjoy that?
Billy:	Yeah! It was great!
Cameraman:	Well, we got it all on film. So if you watch the television news tonight you'll see it all over again.
Billy:	Fancy our family being on the telly! What a prize, Dad! That's the best prize we'll ever win!
Mum:	*(Laughing.)* Even better than free chocolate for life?

Hazel Townson

Down to Earth

Setting

Earth a million years ago; the Hobhorn planet and a modern ring road.

Characters

Danu, gentle giantess; twelve Hobhorns; Hobhorn Queen; Daughter; Mum; Son; Dad.

Production notes

Although this play is written for twelve Hobhorns, the parts can be adjusted to suit more or less children.

Prologue

(Earth, a million years ago.)

Danu:
I am Danu, the gentle giantess
Who guards the Horn of Plenty,
Where everyone can come to take what
nourishment they need.
There is enough for everyone, unless
Someone takes selfishly, in greed.
That is the careful watch I keep.
But now I sleep.

All Hobhorns:
We are the Hobhorns who live on the mountain,
We take what we want for our pleasure.
We don't care about the future
Or any other creature,
We don't care a fig for Danu's law –
We take what we want and we want more.

Hobhorn Queen: Drink yourselves silly! Gorge yourselves sick!
Take and take and take and take.
Load up the wagons till the axles break.

(Their last couplet is taken up as a chant by all the Hobhorns as they plunder the Horn of Plenty. Exit staggering.)

Danu:
I wake to find the Horn of Plenty
Broken and empty.
How dare they do this? So selfishly, so stupidly
To spill and spoil a gift that cannot ever be replaced.
I am Danu, the gentle giantess,
But now I put aside my gentleness.
My anger gives me wild strength.
With my bare hands I'll tear this mountain from its base
And hurl all Hobhorns into outer space.

(The Hobhorns cling together, terrified. Danu finally uproots their mountain and flings them into space. Exit with fading 'Aargh!')

Danu: My strength is gone, my life is done.
I gave the land my love and now
I fold my body in. *(She dies.)*

Scene 1

(The Hobhorns spin on, clinging together and fall in a heap. They are on their own planet out in space. The Queen rises.)

Hobhorn Queen: Bah! I hate it! I watch the Earth from far out in the dark where Danu flung us, and I hate it. For thousands of years I've wanted nothing but revenge: Earth's ruin, that's all I dream of. Hobhorns the time has come. You! You! And You! Prepare for our first mission to Earth.

Hobhorn 1: Us mistress?

Hobhorn 2: Fabulous!

Hobhorn 3: Wicked!

Hobhorn 4: Poison, sludge and slime, this is gonna be good!

Hobhorn Queen: Shut up, all of you, and answer me: what is the aim of your mission?

Hobhorn 6: To poison the rivers!

Hobhorn 7: To fill the oceans with contaminating sludge!

Hobhorn 8: To choke the air!

Hobhorn 9: To leach the living heart out of the soil!

Hobhorn 10: To ruin the planet Earth!

Hobhorn Queen: Correct. But because of the ancient curse of Danu we cannot, by ourselves, ruin Earth. So what do we do?

All Hobhorns: We get the humans to do it for us.

Hobhorn Queen: Correct. You will be working among the humans. They are strange creatures. They are stupid. Stupid and weak. Name three human weaknesses.

Hobhorn 10: Greed!

Hobhorn 11: Selfishness!

Hobhorn 12: Despair!

Hobhorn Queen: Use these to get what you want. Do anything to ruin Earth forever. I want no failures. To the launching pad.

(She places the Hobhorns on catapult launching pads made from other Hobhorns and pulls the levers. The Hobhorns shoot out into space.)

Hobhorn 1: Aargh! I'm spinning round like a Catherine wheel... oooh, now I'm falling... Earth is rushing towards me...

I'm falling... fields and rivers and a tiny city... I'm falling, falling... streets and cars and... oh no... a huge – flat – concrete – roof! A multi-storey car-park! Aargh!

(The Hobhorn crashes through the roof, and sprawls on the floor.)

Scene 2

(A ring road somewhere on Earth.)

Hobhorn 1: What a landing. Oh well, better get started. First off, I could do with some wheels. What's this? A brand new Ducatti 1000. Mm... twin carbs, horizontal cams, power-assisted steering. Nice bike. I'll take it. Ignition? No problem: one twist of my Hobhorn fingernail. *(Starts the motorbike and roars down the ramp on to the ring road.)* Filth and poison. Feel the wind on my horn. I'm cruising baby. And what's that in front? An estate-car, with a nice little family sitting inside like four fat ducks.

(The car contains Mum, Dad, Daughter and Son. Dad blows his nose and throws the tissue out of the window. Mum pops a sweet in her mouth and throws out the wrapper. Son finishes a chocolate bar and throws out the wrapper. Daughter finishes a canned drink and throws out the can.)

Hobhorn 1: Tissue. Sweet papers. A kingsize chocky-bar wrapper. An empty can of coke. Oh this is promising. *(The family continue to throw out litter as the Hobhorn lists each thing.)* One can of orange, two salt n' vinegar crisp packets, five crumpled pieces of newspaper, two pots of curry sauce and mushy peas, four funsize chocky-bar wrappers, three wooden forks and three polystyrene takeaway trays! Filth and poison, what a welcome to Earth! This is fabulous! Wicked! *(Hobhorn moves alongside the car and shouts through the window.)* Hey you lot! Keep it up! Fabulous work.

Daughter: Mum, I've had enough of my curry, chips and peas.

Mum: Chuck them away then duckie.

Hobhorn 1: Can you hear me? I said – Ugh!

(A tray of curry and chips hits the Hobhorn full in the face. The motorbike swerves out of control and crashes. The Hobhorn lies motionless.)

Hobhorn 1: Hobhorns don't die. We always get up again. *(Points to motorbike.)* And that's another piece of junk. There must be 80,000 people in this city. Just think about it. If they all chucked as much as that lot out of their car-windows, the roads would be feet deep in rubbish before you could say pollution. A city buried in its own litter. Round one to me eh?

Tony Jones

The sleepers of Thorb

Setting

Mark's parents' farm; the planet Szarb and a Thorbian city.

Characters

Mark, son of Mr and Mrs Wright; Laura Donaldson; Mr Wright, a farmer; Mrs Wright, his wife; voice of the Szarbians; a Thorbian robot; Cedrox, a the Thorbian leader; Thorbians; Flashes.

Scenery and props

A table; chairs; a teapot; mugs; coloured lights; a large box covered with iridescent metallic paper and five different coloured ribbons; a barrier across one side of the stage (perhaps corrugated card, painted and decorated); various pieces of scientific looking equipment; a box large enough for a child to lie down in; sound effects tape; simple masks.

Production notes

This drama for nine- to twelve-year-olds involves careful planning of special effects. The children need to decide how to achieve the effects of the Szarbian coloured lights and assorted 'space-age' noises. The flashes can be played by children dressed in brightly coloured clothes.

Scene 1

(Mark's parents' farm.)

Mark: What are you doing down on the farm, Laura? Do you realise you're trespassing?

Laura: Sorry!

Mark: My dad said the next trespasser he catches he'll report to the police. *(Officiously.)* You'd better come with me.

Laura: Come with you?

Mark: To see my dad.

(Mark takes Laura to his parents' farmhouse. They mime talking.)

Mr Wright: We've been looking for you, Mark. Have you fed the hens yet?

Mark: No... but.... Dad, I've caught a trespasser.

Mr Wright: *(Sees Laura for the first time.)* Hello, it's Laura Donaldson isn't it?

Laura: Yes.

Mr Wright: Would you like a hot cup of tea? You look cold.

Mrs Wright: *(Entering from the kitchen.)* I've just put the kettle on, it's freezing outside.

Mark:	*(Interrupting.)* But Dad, I caught her on our land.
Mr Wright:	Yes, but Mark, the Donaldsons are our friends.
Mark:	But....
Laura:	*(Interrupting.)* I was keeping close to the hedge, over by the sub-station.
Mark:	She claimed she saw these weird flashes.
Mr Wright:	What kind of flashes?
Laura:	Like lightning, only they were all different colours – red, blue, green, yellow and gold.
Mr Wright:	*(Laughs.)* There's an army place near here. Some kind of exercise, no doubt.
Mrs Wright:	Here's your tea, Laura.
Mr Wright:	Feed the hens, Mark. Their food is in the outhouse.
Mark:	Come on Laura, you'll have to help me. *(Laura leaves her cup of tea, untouched. They go outside.)*
Mark:	I really thought my dad would have a go at you for trespassing. *(Excited.)* Look... up in the sky. Flashes!
Mark:	They're heading towards us. Run! Run to the house!

(The coloured flashes surround the children.)

Scene 2

(On another planet that is just rock and dust, the children see a large, iridescent box.)

Laura:	Where are we?
Mark:	I... I don't know.

(A voice inside the box speaks.)

Voice:	You are on the planet Szarb.
Mark:	You speak English?
Voice:	We speak all your languages. We are the Szarbians. Thousand of years ago an alien race came and took over our planet. They turned a wonderful place into this dust bowl. We fought back but they trapped us inside this box. We brought you here to open the box and release us. We cannot open it by ourselves.
Mark:	How did you get into the box?
Voice:	They used their magic on us but by doing so they destroyed themselves. Their ruined cities are the other side of the desert, beyond those buildings to the right. In time we found a way to seep out of the box – turn ourselves into colourful lights and explore the universe.

Laura: That's how you found us?

Voice: Yes, you are intelligent creatures who can help us.

Mark: Well, I am. I'm not sure if you'd call Laura intell....

Voice: There is no time for humour. We have waited too long already. We can turn ourselves into light... that is something we have taken thousands of years to do... but we cannot become our real selves. We are still trapped in the box. There are five of us and we need to be free. Help us!

Laura: We would, if we knew how. *(Examines the box.)* How do we open the box?

Voice: Walk towards the ruined cities. Before you get to the buildings, there is a giant barrier – a force field. Destroy it and the box will open. Take care, creatures of Earth. Do not go into the ruins, they will be unsafe.

Mark: We will take care.

(They walk across the desert towards a barrier at the side of the stage. There is a hum, like the buzzing of bees.)

The horrible aliens that trapped these poor Szarbians inside the box had a high degree of technology.

Laura: While Earth's creatures were crawling out of their primeval slime. Unless, of course, it was the other way round. Unless the creatures that built the city were the natural inhabitants of Szarb.

Mark: Laura, you and your imagination.

Laura: Aliens do not build cities, they invade and destroy.

Mark: Yes, true.

Laura: The Szarbians said...

(A flash of light spins around Laura and Mark.)

Voice: We can read your minds. Think nothing, do as you are told.

Laura: Why should we?

Voice: Because we have the power to hurt.

Laura: Hurt then!

(Mark and Laura suddenly double up in pain.)

Laura: My head, oh my poor head hurts.

Mark: My leg... I can't move my leg.

Voice: You will obey us.

Mark: Yes.

(At the barrier.)

Laura:	They are evil creatures, but we have no choice.
Mark:	No choice. Still, they can have this planet. It's ruined.
Laura:	As long as we get back to Earth.
Mark:	How do we destroy the barrier?
Voice:	Look for a switch, you fools.
Laura:	We'll walk along the barrier. It must end.
Mark:	There will be a lever or something, to switch off the power.
Laura:	I can't see the box now. The barrier curves, all its energy is focused on the box.
Mark:	It ends... there's a large switch.
Laura:	Great.
Voice:	Don't do anything foolish, or you will regret it.
Laura:	Quick Mark, the other side of the barrier. Run.

(Laura runs around the barrier, Mark follows.)

Mark:	Want another headache?
Laura:	But the Szarbians can't reach us here.
Mark:	How do you know?
Laura:	The force field beats them back... what they said was all bluff.
Mark:	How do you know?
Laura:	They can explore the universe... but not the city. If they could, they'd have turned off the barrier's powers themselves. Look!

Scene 3

(Laura and Mark find themselves in a city, in front of a flight of stairs.)

Laura:	Let's go down these stairs.

(Mark and Laura mime walking down a staircase.)

Mark:	Down into more ruins! There may be five-fanged, three-eyed monsters down in the depths, waiting to gobble us up.
Laura:	I haven't seen a single creature yet, or even heard a bird sing.
Mark:	That's because they're all waiting down those steps that are millions of years old.
Laura:	Come on!

(The children walk down the stairs. Suddenly the stage is lit up.)

Mark:	Wow!
Laura:	The whole place is lit up.

Mark:	Yes, but not by electricity. It's not been occupied for millions of years, if we believe the Szarbians.
Laura:	The city must have been magnificent.
Mark:	Laura, this is a tomb. This is like finding a Pharaoh's tomb.
Laura:	This is so sad. They've been dead for millions of years – an entire people wiped out.
Mark:	Yet, they expected to live again, just like the Egyptian pharaohs did. Why else would they have gone to so much trouble making this tomb? Their technology is so great that everything here still works, even after millions of years.
Laura:	Mark... look!

(A robot walks towards them.)

Robot:	Welcome. Look, watch the pictures.

(Beyond Laura and Mark is a tableau of human-like creatures, dressed in white robes, eating, playing and generally happy. Monsters appear. They are large, with bulging frog-like eyes and toad-like skins. From their fingers they produce 'flashes' that hurt and destroy the human creatures.)

These are Szarbians. They came to destroy the planet Thorb and the Thorbians. They even called our planet Szarb. That is an insult. Look... see how the remaining Thorbians fought back. (*Mark and Laura see six Thorbs left working in a laboratory.*) See the grey-haired Thorb – he's our leader Cedrox. *(The robot points to where a Thorbian lies asleep in a box.)* He invented the great barrier that beat the Szarbians. All Szarbians died, save five. Our leader wanted them kept in a box, inside a force-field. They were frozen in time – to show the Thorbians that evil never wins.

Laura:	So why is Cedrox lying in a tomb?
Robot:	He's not in a tomb. He is alive. I have to activate him. I am programmed to awake when anyone enters this chamber. Then I must tell the newcomers our history. Now I have to awaken the leader of the Thorbs.

(The robot walks over to the 'coffin' and presses various buttons. Cedrox sits up in his 'coffin' and rubs his eyes, as if he has been in a long sleep.)

Cedrox:	Greetings, travellers.
Robot:	You have waited a long time, Cedrox.
Laura:	We saw what happened to your planet.
Cedrox:	We were almost destroyed... but we beat them.
Robot:	The Thorbian technology is superior to all else.
Cedrox:	Yes, but the Szarbians poisoned our planet. Their planet was ruined by their wars, so they came to take ours. Their

poisons turned much of it to desert. We created a force-field around the city and decided to sleep until the planet could sustain life again. All our animals are still in 'sleep'.

Laura: You have lived for millions of years.

Cedrox: Yes! *(Laughs.)* That is a record! You now have the technology to arrive here. You have done well.

Mark: The Szarbians brought us here. They turned themselves into glorious flashes and have crossed through space to reach us.

Cedrox: We may yet lose. How silly my pride! I wanted the Szarbians in the box to be a monument to our greatness. What a fool I have been. *(Thinks.)* Robot, increase the force-field. Destroy the box and the creatures inside.

Robot: Yes, leader. *(The Robot exits but soon returns.)*

Robot: I am destroyed, Master.

Cedrox: What happened?

Robot: They knew I was coming, as I touched the switch their flashing-fingers touched me. The box exploded.

Cedrox: And?

Robot: The barrier exploded, too. The charge went through me. I am near my end.

Cedrox: You have served us well.

Laura: He is dying....

(Robot collapses.)

Cedrox: But the Szarbians are destroyed too. They could never survive the power that went through them.

Mark: Let's go and see.

Cedrox: All of us together. If I am wrong, we will all perish.

(They walk back past the barrier.)

Laura: They've died, they've died.

Cedrox: We have a saucer to get you home.

Scene 4

Mrs Wright: Have you fed the hens yet, Mark?

Mark: Not quite.

Mrs Wright: You'd both better hurry and feed the hens. Laura, your cup of tea will be cold.

Laura: *(To Mark.)* All the time we were on Thorb and we've lost virtually no Earth time at all.

Keith West

WORK AND PLAY

Scenarios

Get home safe!

Setting

A busy road.

Characters

Groups of children.

Production notes

Mock up a road circuit in the hall using games lines for or tape for roads.

Tell the children that while they were at school, machines took over the world. All the grown ups are asleep. Cars, buses and lorries are running by themselves and will catch them if they can. They have to cross busy roads to get home. If they use the Green Cross Code they'll be safe.

Children can then take turns to be vehicles and to be the children crossing the roads.

Tell the children who are miming vehicles to walk round the circuit all the time, making appropriate noises. They are to catch the crossers, by touching them, if they can, but it doesn't count if they run. They must also stay on the road.

The difficulty of the task can be controlled by varying the number of vehicles in relation to the length of road. It should never be made so difficult as to encourage risk taking.

The scenario can be organised as a team game with points given for roads crossed, to encourage road safety.

Alan Brown

Willie's wallet

Setting

An ordinary street.

Characters

Willie; Jane; Soraya; Sam; Old Lady; Mrs Brown; people in the bus queue.

Scenery and props

A wallet; a large hanky; a bulging shopping bag or basket; a newspaper; a bus stop sign (optional).

Willie is walking to work. He pulls out his hanky from his pocket but doesn't notice that he pulls out his wallet as well. The wallet falls on to the pavement but Willy doesn't notice and continues on his way.

Jane and Soraya come along. Soraya sees the wallet and picks it up. She shows it to Jane. Jane says they must take it to the police station and puts it in her pocket. She suggests they take the bus to the police station as it is quite a long way off. The two girls join a bus queue.

Sam joins the queue. He sees the wallet poking out of Jane's pocket and steals it while Jane is chatting to Soraya, putting it into his jacket pocket.

More people join the bus queue, including an Old Lady with a heavy shopping bag who stands right behind Sam. The Old Lady sets the shopping bag down, and begins chatting with the people in the queue. She tells them she is very tired and doesn't feel very well. She has found it a real struggle to get the shopping done and her bag is very heavy. Suddenly the Old Lady clutches her head and groans. Then she falls to the ground, grabbing at Sam's jacket to try and save herself. Sam swings round and the wallet falls unnoticed into the Old Lady's shopping bag.

Everyone, including Sam, gathers round to help the Old Lady. They prop her up and she slowly begins to recover. Someone fans her with a newspaper, and someone else offers to call an ambulance, but the Old Lady says she'll be all right; she just wants to go home. Someone in the queue has an idea. There is a house near the bus stop. He/she runs to the house to get help. Mrs Brown comes to the door and is told what has happened. She says that her husband, who works at a shop nearby, will be able to borrow the shop van to drive the Old Lady home.

Mrs Brown hurries off and fetches her husband who turns out to be Willie. Willie still has not realised that he has lost his wallet. Willie helps the Old Lady up and leads her towards the van. Then somebody realises the shopping bag has been left behind, runs after them with it, slips and spills the bag's contents at Willie's feet. Willie's wallet falls out on to the pavement. Willie sees his wallet, looks surprised and thinks he has just dropped it. He holds the wallet up with a big smile. 'That was a near thing! Nearly lost my wallet in the excitement!' he says.

Hazel Townson

Improvisations

The first three of the following improvisations are suitable for use with younger age groups while the rest are for junior pupils and those who have developed reading fluency. The class could be divided into groups and given one of the situations to improvise. Possible ideas and suggestions are given in italics.

The broken window

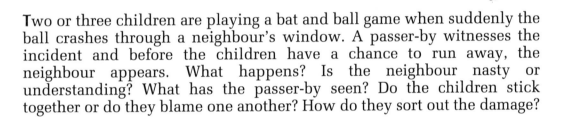

Setting
A residential area.

Characters
Two or three children; a neighbour; a passer-by.

Scenery and props
An indoor bat and ball.

Two or three children are playing a bat and ball game when suddenly the ball crashes through a neighbour's window. A passer-by witnesses the incident and before the children have a chance to run away, the neighbour appears. What happens? Is the neighbour nasty or understanding? What has the passer-by seen? Do the children stick together or do they blame one another? How do they sort out the damage?

Christina Dove

Hats off/hats on

Characters
People who do different jobs.

Scenery and props
A vartiety of hats representing different jobs; a whistle or other device.

Production notes
This improvisation for five- to six-year-olds provides an opportunity for them to develop ideas about people at work.

Tell the children to stand in a circle. Provide each child with a different hat. Tell them to imagine they are the person who normally wears this hat and does the job it represents. They should mime appropriate actions. Blow the whistle as a signal for them to change hats with the person on their right. They can then mime a new character.

Christina Dove

The collision

Setting

A road accident.

Characters

Coach and car drivers; coach and car passengers; emergency services.

Scenery and props

Chairs set out to represent coach seats and car seats; first aid kit.

Production notes

This improvisation for seven- to eight-year-olds can be used to develop basic first aid skills and accident procedure.

There has been a collision between a coach and a car. Injuries are involved. It will be necessary to contact the emergency services. First aid may need to be applied. The police arrive to take statements and control traffic. An ambulance may be needed to take the injured to hospital.

Charles Thomson

Victorian music hall

Setting

A music hall stage.

Characters

A 'straight man'; several 'funny men'.

Production notes

Ask each child to think of an 'I say, I say' or 'Knock knock' joke. Explain that the straight man is trying to recite a poem, but is continually interrupted by the various funny men.

Straight man: 'Daffodils', by William Wordsworth. I wandered...
Funny man: *(Rushing on from side of stage, interrupting.)* I say, I say, I say – what do you call a gorilla with a gun?
Straight man: I don't know, what do you call a gorilla with a gun?
Funny man: Sir! *(Exits, probably laughing hysterically.)*

The straight man becomes progressively more irritated and aggressive and when the final funny man leaves the stage, he sticks his nose in the air and stalks offstage, saying, 'You lot just don't appreciate culture'.

Heather Cawte Winskill

At the market

Setting

A busy open market.

Characters

Shoppers; traders; 'Toby man' (person who collects rent from traders); Health and Safety Inspector; traders' representative.

Scenery and props

Desks or tables, arranged lengthways in aisles; goods for the market stalls; area where children can shout without disturbing other classes.

Production notes

Talk about a local market with the children. What kind of things can you buy there? Why do people go there rather than to the shops? How do traders attract people to their wares? How do they talk to the shoppers to make them buy something?

Split the class into two groups: the shoppers and the traders. The traders should think what they are going to sell. This will depend on the props available unless the children decide to mime selling their wares.

The traders start by developing 'street cries' advertising their wares. *(Perhaps they are selling at a lower price than a rival.)*

Some shoppers have come to this market for the first time; some go every week. Some are with a friend, others are on their own. *(Are they buying something special, just doing the weekly shopping or looking for a bargain?)*

The shoppers can haggle with the traders to see if they can get a lower price, check goods they buy in case there are any faults, look around at the other stalls to see if they can see the same things cheaper elsewhere.

Now try developing a story-line. For example, the 'Toby man', hands out a letter one morning explaining that the market is moving to another site in town, and all the rents are to be doubled. *(Can the traders afford the new rents? Will the shoppers have further to travel? Will prices go up?)*

'A' steals a bike and sells it to the second-hand stall. The trader doesn't know it's stolen until a shopper recognises it. What happens?

'B' is the Health and Safety Inspector. Are any of the traders going to get caught out? *(Perhaps a shopper has been sold a dangerous second-hand toaster, or caught salmonella from the eggs.)*

'C' is the National Federation of Market Traders representative, whose job is to help sort out disputes. 'C' also sells useful things like stall covers, price tags, fluorescent card for advertising and marker pens.

Nick Pollard

Half a team

Setting

A football club.

Characters

Nick; Dinger; Jackie; Jaz; Edward; other players.

Scenery and props

A football (optional).

Production notes

This is a dramatic situation for improvisation from Michael Hardcastle's novel *Half a Team* (Methuen). The characters named are boys, but there's no reason why they should not be renamed as girls. It's a classic struggle for power between the members of a football team and is suitable for use with nine- to twelve-year-olds. The role play is suited to groups of three to about twelve children.

Before the activity, photocopy the character descriptions, cut them out and give them to the appropriate players. Keep the situation description yourself. Write down on a piece of paper the following line from the novel: 'You going to stand down as skipper then, Nick?' Read the situation description to the group. Then ask each character to tell the team who they are, starting with the other players (who must be named). When this is complete, ask Nick and Dinger to explain to the team what they think their tactics should be for the five-a-side festival. At an appropriate place in the discussion pass Dinger the line from the novel.

The situation

The Oakland Rangers are going to field a team in the five-a-side festival. In the past they played in an eleven-a-side Sunday league, but got no higher than sixth. They could lose matches in the league and still play every week, but the festival is a knock-out competition. Will Rangers need new tactics?

Nick

You are a striker and are acknowledged as the best player in the locality. After proving yourself in Superstars you were voted captain of Rangers. 'I won the right to make the decisions. It's my job to do what's best for the team. That's what a captain's for – to lead.' In the festival you want to play a waiting game, letting the opposition tire themselves out before going all out to score. You don't see a need to discuss these tactics with anybody, least of all the goalie.

Dinger

You are a strong mid-field player; you were runner-up to Nick in Superstars and are now vice-captain of Rangers. You want to have a say in the decisions affecting the team, particularly tactics for the festival. You want to go all out from the start. 'I say that if we play Nick's way, we'll only play one match. We'll be knocked out of the competition almost before it's begun. Oakland Rangers will be finished.' You are willing to put your ideas to the vote, and to replace Nick as captain.

Jackie Allerton

You are the goalie, and you are fed up with being treated as a nobody. You think that saving goals is as important as scoring them and that your views should be taken into account.

Jaz Fagan

You are a winger and are fed up with losing matches. You hope that changing to five-a-side will give you more chance to score and be a 'star'.

Edward Lancaster

You are a mid-fielder and, like Jaz, are fed up with losing matches. You agree with Jaz in thinking that playing five-a-side might give you more opportunity for goal-scoring and stardom.

The other players from the eleven-a-side squad

You all know that in the festival only five players and a substitute will be picked. You all want to be chosen.

Michael Hardcastle

Dramatic poems and dialogues

The marching band

Characters

Musicians in a band.

Scenery and props

Simple musical instruments; flags.

Production notes

This piece can be used to help teach children about several instruments as well as provide an imaginative movement experience. First, read the poem to the children and use records or tapes to demonstrate what each instrument sounds like. Look at pictures of the instruments or real ones, if possible, to give pupils an idea of how they are played. Let them practise miming the playing of the instruments and mimicking the sounds. Assign some children to be each instrument and some to handle the flags.

(Start the poem with everyone seated and each group playing at the appropriate time. For the second part, each group rises in turn, plays their instruments, and marches around so that eventually everyone is part of the parade.)

Part 1

Let's hear the drums
With their rat-a-tat-tat.
Let's hear the tambourine.
Let's hear the trombone
And the piccolo.
Let's see the flags wave red
    and green.

Part 2

Drums...
Tambourines...
Trombones...
Piccolos...
Flags...
Everyone...
It's the best marching band
    I've ever seen!

Carol Ann Piggins

Well, what happened?

Characters

Two children.

Production notes

This dialogue is intended for two voices and the parts are indicated by two different type styles. No special scenery is needed. The poem can be used with seven- to eight-year-olds.

'I raised my voice,
he raised his fist.
I called him names,
he twisted my wrist.'

*'I held his arm,
he kicked my shin.
I said I'd get mad
if he didn't pack it in.'*

'He pulled my nose,
I belted his ear.
He said you'd better
get out of here.'

*'I told him my brother
would give him a clout.
He said his big sister
would sort me out.'*

'We argued and fought,
we shouted and swore.
I told him my dad
would give him what for.'

*'We rolled on the ground,
we clinched and we kicked,
till someone said, Watch it,
you'll both be nicked.'*

'And that's when you came, sir
and pulled us away,
but we're friends now, aren't we?
We've stood here all play.'

Brian Moses

The gerbil's funeral

Characters

Narrator; eight children – three boys and five girls; teacher.

All children: The gerbil's going bald, Miss,
The gerbil's lost its hair,
Its neck and face and ears, Miss
Are practically bare!

Oooh, Miss, what if she dies?
What if, after all,
She's suffering from the plague, Miss?
We could have a funeral!

Narrator: Who'll bring the coffin?

Child 1:   'I',

Narrator: said Robin.

Child 1:   'I've got a box that I'm not usin'.
I'll bring the coffin.'

Narrator: Who'll dig the grave?

Child 2:   'I',

Narrator: said Dave,

Child 2:   'With my dad's spade,
I'll dig the grave.'

Narrator: Who'll sing a dirge?

Child 3:   'I',

Narrator: said Jim,

Child 3:   'I can sing a solemn hymn.
I'll sing a dirge.'

Narrator: Who'll be chief mourner?

Child 4:   'I',

Narrator: said Lorna.

Child 4:   'I'm the one who brought her.
I'll be chief mourner.'

Narrator:	Who'll make the cross?
Child 5:	'I',
Narrator:	said Claire.
Child 5:	'I'll carve it with care. I'll make the cross.'
Narrator:	Who'll bring the flowers?
Children 6, 7 & 8:	'I',
Narrator:	said Rose and Daisy and Heather...
All children:	What about me? What about me? What about me?
Narrator:	All the boys and the girls Fell to fighting and to shouting –
Narrator:	Who'll be the preacher?
Teacher:	'I',
Narrator:	said the teacher.
Teacher:	'I'll be the preacher, If the need arises. Meanwhile, we'll hope for the best. Life's full of surprises. Now, what about this spelling test?'

June Crebbin

On a Monday morning

Characters

Two groups, singing to the tune of 'What shall we do with the drunken sailor?'

Group A: What shall we do with a naughty schoolboy?
What shall we do with a naughty schoolboy?
What shall we do with a naughty schoolboy
On a Monday morning?

Group B: Throw him in the bin with the mouldy rubbish,
Throw him in the bin with the mouldy rubbish,
Throw him in the bin with the mouldy rubbish
On a Monday morning.

All: Oh, dear, the smell's disgusting!
Oh, dear, the smell's disgusting!
Oh, dear, the smell's disgusting
On a Monday morning!

Group A: What shall we do with a naughty schoolgirl?
What shall we do with a naughty schoolgirl?
What shall we do with a naughty schoolgirl
On a Monday morning?

Group B: Hang her from the ceiling and tickle her tootsies,
Hang her from the ceiling and tickle her tootsies,
Hang her from the ceiling and tickle her tootsies
On a Monday morning.

All: Oh, dear, the smell's disgusting!
Oh, dear, the smell's disgusting!
Oh, dear, the smell's disgusting
On a Monday morning!

Group A: What shall we do with an angry teacher?
What shall we do with an angry teacher?
What shall we do with an angry teacher
On a Monday morning?

Group B: Lock her in the cupboard with a hungry tiger,
Lock her in the cupboard with a hungry tiger,
Lock her in the cupboard with a hungry tiger
On a Monday morning.

All: Oh, dear, the smell's disgusting!
Open up the door, the smell's disgusting!
Here comes the tiger – and the tiger's smiling!
On a Monday morning.

June Crebbin

Scripted drama

Mr Egbert Nosh

Setting

A street.

Characters

Narrator; Egbert Nosh; Egbert's house; Bus Driver; Egbert's garage; Egbert's dustbin.

Production notes

This simple humorous play is suitable across the primary age range. The part of the narrator can be taken either by the teacher or by a child with an appropriate reading ability. The children might like to devise simple costumes, such as a peaked cap for the bus driver and large pieces of card painted appropriately for the house, garage and dustbin.

Narrator:	Once upon a time there was a man called Egbert Nosh, Mr Egbert Nosh. Now Egbert Nosh lived in a house. The house was in a street with other houses. Egbert liked his house best; he thought it was the best house in the road. That is, until one day.... Well, one day Egbert Nosh went out for a walk. He had not gone far when he heard footsteps behind him. Very heavy footsteps. *(Footsteps.)* He looked round to see who was behind him. And what do you think he saw? Yes, there was his house walking down the street.
Egbert:	This is ridiculous.
Narrator:	Said Egbert.
House:	Why?
Narrator:	Asked the house.
Egbert:	Houses don't go for walks.
House:	This house does. Where are you going?
Egbert:	I'm going to.... Why should I tell a house where I am going?
House:	I want to come with you.
Egbert:	You can't. You're not a dog. Go back home at once.
House:	Not unless you do.
Egbert:	I'm not going back.
House:	Then I shall stay here with you.

Egbert: This is ridiculous.

Narrator: He felt such a fool standing in the middle of the street talking to a house. So he went back home. The house went after him. *(Footsteps.)* Now what could he do? He couldn't have his house with him every time he went out. He had to visit friends. He had to go to the shops. He had to go to work. Then an idea came to him. Quietly, very quietly he opened the front door. Even more quietly he shut it. Then he ran down the path and to the bus stop round the corner as fast as he could. But what do you think he found when he got round the corner? Yes, his house was waiting for him.

Egbert: This is ridiculous.

House: Coo, I'm puffed. *(Heavy breathing.)*

Egbert: What are you doing here?

House: Waiting for a bus.

Egbert: Houses don't go on buses.

House: This house does.

Narrator: Just then a bus drew up.

Driver: *(Bus draws up.)* Is this your house, sir?

Egbert: Yes, I'm afraid it is.

Driver: It is not regulation size to come on the bus, sir. Sorry. *(Bus drives off.)*

Egbert: Now I've missed my bus.

House: Come on, race you home. *(Running footsteps.)*

Narrator: Egbert was very cross when he got back. Then he had an idea. He would disguise himself. He put on a big hat and a beard. Then he went out. He had just reached the corner when....

House: Have you shaved today?

Narrator: Yes, it was the house.

Egbert: This is ridiculous.

House: Can I dress up too?

Egbert: No, you can't!

Narrator: So the house went back home with Egbert. Now what could he do? He went to bed to think. Then he had an idea. He would wait till it was dark. Then the house would not see him. That night he crept out. He forgot he was still in his pyjamas. He crept down the path on his hands and knees. Then he stopped. Not a sound. Now he was in the street. He stopped. Not a sound. Now he was at the corner. He stopped. Not a sound. He went to get up to run. But something was on his pyjama leg. Yes, it was the foot of the house.

Egbert:	This is ridic....
House:	Sh! You'll wake up all the girls and boys.
Egbert:	But...
Narrator:	Just then he heard something else. *(Creaking noise.)*
Egbert:	Who's there with you?
Garage:	It's me.
Narrator:	Said the garage.
Egbert:	Oh, no!
Garage:	If the house can go for a walk at night, why can't I?
Narrator:	Now there was another noise. *(Clanking noise.)*
Egbert:	Who else is there?
Dustbin:	It's me.
Narrator:	Said the dustbin.
Egbert:	Oh, no. This really is ridiculous.
Dustbin:	I don't like being left on my own in the dark.
Egbert:	Come on. We must all go back home and sort this out. *(Footsteps. Creaking noise. Clanking noise.)*
Narrator:	When he got back home Egbert thought very hard. Then he had an idea.
Egbert:	Look. If I take you out on Sundays, can I go out on my own for the rest of the week?
House:	I'll think about it. Can I go to the park?
Egbert:	Well, it will look a bit silly.
House:	If you call me silly, I'll follow you everywhere.
Egbert:	Oh, all right, I'll take you to the park.
House:	With the garage?
Egbert:	If he must.
House:	And the dustbin?
Egbert:	Oh, I suppose so.
House:	Goodie, goodie! *(Creaking and clanking noise. Cries of 'Goodie!')*
Narrator:	So if ever you go to call on Egbert Nosh, don't go on a Sunday, because his house won't be there; nor will his garage; nor will his dustbin. And you'll know where they are, won't you?

Paul Groves

Kind King Peter

Setting

Kind King Peter's palace; the village and the village school; the King's bedroom; Uncle Toby's house and the balcony of the palace.

Characters

Narrator; King Peter; Postmistress; Policeman; Milkman; Sam the guard; Doctor; Uncle Toby; Children.

Scenery and props

Tape of music; soldier's helmet; crown; doctor's bag; bottle of medicine; loudspeaker (a cone made from card).

Production notes

This play is particularly suited to younger primary children. Let the children help design and make the costumes and choose the incidental music. They can also add their own ideas to the play. For example, they might like to think of other ways in which King Peter can say good night and good morning, for example, telephone, television, post and so on.

Scene 1

(Kind King Peter's palace.)

Narrator:	Kind King Peter was a very kind king. He always said 'Good morning' and 'Good night' to everyone in his kingdom. Every morning he opened his bedroom door and said...
King Peter:	Good morning!
Narrator:	...to all his servants. Then, as he left the castle he said...
King Peter:	Good morning!
Narrator:	...to Sam the guard. He would then walk to the village. Once there he would say...

Scene 2

(The village and village school.)

King Peter:	Good morning!
Narrator:	...to the postmistress...
Postmistress:	Good morning, Your Majesty.
Narrator:	...the policeman...
Policeman:	Good morning, Your Majesty.
Narrator:	...and the milkman.
Milkman:	Er, good morning, Your Majesty.

Narrator:	Next, he popped into the village school and said...
King Peter:	Good morning!
Narrator:	...to all the children. And the children replied...
Children:	Good morning, Your Majesty.
Narrator:	When night came, King Peter said...
King Peter:	Good night!
Narrator:	...to the children, the milkman, the policeman, the postmistress, to Sam the guard and all his servants. But when he had finished saying...
King Peter:	Good night!
Narrator:	...kind King Peter was too tired to eat supper, and he went straight to bed.

Scene 3

(The King is asleep, snoring in his bedroom.)

Narrator:	*(Over snoring.)* One day, King Peter did not wake up.
King Peter:	*(Snoring.)* Zzzzzz!
Narrator:	*(Over snoring.)* Everyone was very worried. When the doctor arrived, Sam the guard asked...
Sam:	Why is he so tired?
Doctor:	I don't know...
Narrator:	...replied the doctor...
Doctor:	...I've pinched him and shaken him. I've shouted Boo! in his ear, but he still won't wake up.
Narrator:	The doctor did not know what to do. Then Sam the guard had an idea.
Sam:	I'll ask Uncle Toby!

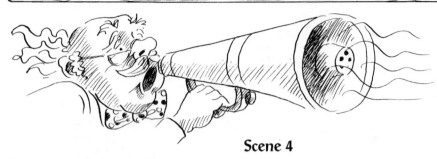

Scene 4

(Uncle Toby's house.)

Narrator: Uncle Toby was an inventor and he was very clever. He gave Sam a bottle of medicine for the King. And he gave him something that looked like a trumpet.

Sam: What's that for, Toby?

Narrator: ...asked Sam.

Uncle Toby: It's called a loudspeaker...

Narrator: ...explained Uncle Toby.

Uncle Toby: You speak through the narrow end and your voice comes out very loud the other end – like this. BOO! *(Loud echo.)*

Narrator: His voice came out so loud it blew Sam's helmet off.

Scene 5

(The King's bedroom.)

Narrator: Sam poured a spoonful of Uncle Toby's medicine into the King's mouth. Straight away King Peter woke up. He jumped out of bed and said...

King Peter: *(Yawning.)* Ah! Now I feel much better. Quick! I must say good morning to everyone!

Narrator: Sam gave him the loudspeaker.

Sam: Try doing it with this.

Narrator: King Peter ran out on to the balcony and shouted...

King Peter: *(Shouting through his loudspeaker.)* Good morning, everyone!

Narrator: ...through the loudspeaker. And everyone in the Kingdom shouted back...

All: Good morning, Your Majesty!

(Incidental music.)

Narrator: *(Over music.)* Then King Peter sat down and ate the biggest breakfast you ever saw – and he was never ill again.

John Walsh

He'd better pay up

Setting

In front of Fred's house.

Characters

Fisherman Fred; Painter Pat; Pat's assistant; adults in the street: Albert, Marina, Mrs Burgin, Mr Benson, Jim Reed, Mary Whitaker and Mr Murphy; cheeky children.

Scenery and props

A table; a bicycle; step-ladders and one or two items of sign-writer's equipment (optional); some packages supposedly containing fish. The main requirement is the sign itself: FRESH FISH SOLD HERE. This can be inscribed on a suitable surface during the performance. Also required are four pieces of card to conceal the four words as events unfold.

Production notes

This play can be performed by a class of seven- to eight-year-olds.

Albert:	*(Coming up to Fred.)* Hi, Fred, how are you?
Fisherman Fred:	Not so bad. But that storm last night nearly filled my boat. I was sitting in water up to my knees.
Albert:	Did you catch many fish?
Fisherman Fred:	Quite a few – worse luck.
Albert:	Worse luck, Fred? What do you mean by that?
Fisherman Fred:	Well, now I've got to sell them all.
Albert:	Don't you like it?
Fisherman Fred:	Of course I don't. I have to go squeaking and wobbling round the streets on this bike calling 'Fish for sale! Fish for sale!' It nearly kills me.
Marina:	*(Strolling up.)* Hey – why don't you open a little shop –

sell your fish there? You could use your house. *(She indicates it.)* Yes, you could use your own front room.

Albert: On a day like this you could even sell it here on the pavement.

Marina: You'd need a notice – to let people know.

Fisherman Fred: Yes, I can just imagine it – my goodness yes. I could have it done in big blue letters. *(Loudly and with an expansive gesture towards the house.)* FISH!

Albert: Or maybe FISH *SOLD*.

Fisherman Fred: *FRESH* FISH SOLD *HERE* – that's what I'll have.

Marina: Do you know Painter Pat who lives down the road? You should get her to come and put up a notice straight away.

Fisherman Fred: You're right. I will.

(Rushes off out of sight. Albert and Marina stroll on their way. Fred is heard crying 'Pat! Pat! I've got a job for you to do!' and Pat's voice is heard discussing it with him. Meanwhile a small group of cheeky children gather outside Fred's house.)

Cheeky children: *(Knock on Fred's door and then start singing.)*
Freddy Morgan sells fish
Fifteen pence a dish.
Don't buy it! Don't buy it!
It stinks when you fry it!

Fisherman Fred: *(Having returned and crept up behind them.)* Clear off, you lot! *(The children flee. Fred, with his hands on his hips, glares after them, not noticing Pat and her assistant coming up behind him.)*

Painter Pat: *(Making Fred jump.)* We're ready to put your notice up. *(They get to work in a businesslike way, inscribing or fixing a FRESH FISH SOLD HERE notice on the front of Fred's house. There is plenty of scope for improvisation; the assistant can be incompetent and draw Pat's fury for putting words in the wrong order. There can also be a hammered thumb and so on! Fred marvels at the notice, but he also busies himself arranging fish on a table outside his house.)* There you are, Fred. What do you think of it, eh?

Fisherman Fred: Great, really great. And it looks like I've got a customer coming.

Painter Pat: There's just one thing – we'd like to be paid.

Fisherman Fred: OK, OK – when I've sold some fish and got some money.

Mrs Burgin: *(Arriving as Painter Pat and her assistant leave.)* Hello Fred. You're starting a shop then, are you? It's a good idea. But there's one thing wrong with that notice of yours – you don't need to say your fish is fresh. We know it's fresh. So you don't need to say so on your sign. *(She goes on her way leaving Fred staring up at the notice.)*

Fisherman Fred: *(Suddenly hurrying off out of sight.)* Pat! Pat! *(We hear him speaking with Pat in the distance.)*

Painter Pat: *(Appearing with Fred and assistant.)* Well, if you really think so, Fred. But we'll have to charge you a little bit extra. *(They add a board to remove the word FRESH from the notice. Fred continues to set out his fish.)* There you are – it's done. So that will be ten... eleven pounds, please.

Fisherman Fred: Yes, I'll pay you, I'll pay you. Ah – here comes another customer. *(Pat and assistant leave discontentedly as Eric Benson comes on the scene.)*

Mr Benson: Mmm – a new notice. I suppose it's OK. But you don't need to have the word HERE on your notice. The notice is here so the fish is here too. That's obvious, isn't it? *(He goes on his way, leaving Fred staring up at the notice.)*

Fisherman Fred: *(Suddenly hurrying off out of sight.)* Pat! Pat! *(We hear him speaking with Pat in the distance.)*

Painter Pat: *(Appearing with Fred and assistant again.)* Well, if you really think so, Fred. But you'll have to pay for all this work. *(They add a board to remove the word HERE from the notice. Fred continues to set out his fish.)* There you are – it's done. So that will be eleven... twelve pounds, please.

Fisherman Fred: Yes, I'll pay you, I'll pay you. Ah – here comes another customer. *(Pat and assistant leave even more discontentedly than they did before.)*

Jim Reed: *(Strolling up to the shop.)* Well, it *looks* all right, that notice of yours. But why say SOLD? We don't expect you to give your fish away free of charge. Don't you think it's a silly word to have on your sign?

(He goes on his way and events are repeated: Fred fetches Pat and assistant, who remove the word SOLD and ask for their money – now thirteen pounds. They leave with an even worse grace when Fisherman Fred fobs them off to deal with his next prospective customer.)

Mary Whitaker: *(Strolling up.)* That board's very smart – well, fairly smart. But why do you have a notice at all? We can tell it's a fish shop just by the smell.

Fisherman Fred: *(Very surly.)* Well I'm not changing it! *(He grumpily rearranges his fish as Mary Whitaker goes on her way.)*

That notice stays!

Cheeky child: *(Passing and seeing the one remaining word on the sign.)* Hello, Mr Fish!

Fisherman Fred: *(Glares at the child and then at the notice. Finally, on an angry impulse, he strides off after Pat and assistant, who remove the one remaining word and ask for their money – now fourteen pounds – more pressingly than ever. They leave in a fury when Fred fobs them off and gets his next 'prospect'.)* Now then, Sir...

Mr Murphy: Well, I don't know whether you can help me at all. I want some light green – to go on my door. Do you have light green?

Fisherman Fred: Light green? I'm sorry – I don't understand.

Mr Murphy: Light green paint – to go on my door. By the way, it's a good idea of yours to open a paint shop. Everyone's been talking about it.

Fisherman Fred: What makes them think I'm starting a paint shop?

Mr Murphy: We've seen Pat coming here with the tins. And we can tell it's a paint shop just by the smell.

Fisherman Fred: *(Leaving Mr Murphy open-mouthed.)* Pat! It's urgent! Pat! I need you! *(Disappears and is heard yelling.)* Pat, I need my notice back. It was right the first time. Please put it back the way it was. Of course I'll pay you. Very soon. All right – twenty pounds... At the start of next week... *(Ad lib. Fred reappears hauling or propelling Pat and assistant to the shop. They restore the notice by removing the overlying boards. Fred and Mr Murphy marvel at the notice as it reappears. Fred is particularly pleased to see it, and is filled with goodwill.)* Oh it's *such* a good sign. And they're such good workers. Always so kind and helpful to me. I don't know what I'd do without them. *(Pat and assistant leave as Fred speaks his final words. They are carrying the four 'blank' boards they have just removed, and as a final* coup de theatre *they reverse them to let the audience read the ominous message* HE'D BETTER PAY UP.*)*

Tony D. Triggs

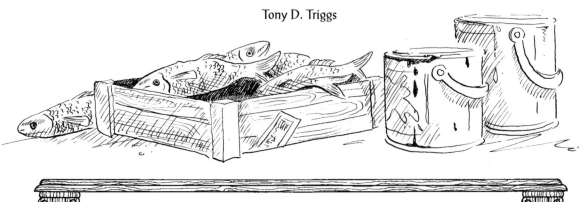

The great egg wheel do-it-yourself play

Setting

A market.

Characters

Either two or seven people.

Scenery and props

An empty egg box; colourful costumes, such as outrageous hats and so on.

Production notes

This is a humorous drama for nine- to twelve-year-olds. If only two children are in the cast, let A play C, E, G, and B play D and F. If seven children are taking part, they should all enter for the final lines.

A: All these stalls. Isn't it exciting?

(Enters carrying an empty egg box.)

B: Where are the eggs?

A: What eggs?

B: The ones you've just seen. Flying like bats, were they?

A: I haven't seen any eggs.

B: Why did you say you had then?

A: I never.

B: Oh, yes you did. You said something about an egg sighting.

A: An egg sighting?

B: Exactly.

(A leaves in disgust, muttering 'Exactly, exactly.')

B: *(Loud and emphatically.)* Eggs actly.

C: *(Enters.)* Where?

B: Don't you start. Where what?

C: Is this enough money?

B: What for? I haven't anything to sell.

C: What? I want to know if anyone can go.

B: Go where?

C: You said someone was acting – is it a good play?

B: No one's acting. No play. Nothing. Bye. *(Exits.)*

C: That's nice, that is. Very polite. Excellent manners, excellent.

D: *(Enters.)* Where and when is it? Is it a car boot sale? I love those.

C: What are you talking about?

D: The sale. Or is it furniture? I'd love to go. Where is it?

C: There isn't one that I know of.

D: Why did you say there was? You were talking about it as I came past.

C: I don't recall anything of the kind. *(Exits.)*

D: Well I never. How very rude. Not a very good example.

E: *(Enters.)* Where are they?

D: Where are what?

E: The sandwiches. I fancy a sandwich. Have they cress in as well?

D: As well as what?

E: As well as egg, of course. Lovely. Where did you say they were?

D: I didn't because I can't. I can't because there aren't any.

E: I could have sworn you said egg sandwich. Bye. *(Exits.)*

D: Some people don't listen properly. Some people are exceedingly stupid. Eggs – heeding! Eggs heeding! That's a good one.

F: *(Enters.)* I'm listening, honest.

D: Pardon?

F: I'm listening. You said to heed you and I am.

D: Oh don't you start. *(Exits.)*

F: I was just being polite. What did she expect?

G: Did it? Where? Does it hurt? Shall I call a doctor?

F: What for?

G: Let me examine you.

F: I'm all right.

G: Where did the egg peck you? Oh no, silly me, it can't.

F: I shall exit. *(Exit.)*

G: *(Calls.)* What did a poor egg ever do to you? Why hit it? It'll break.

B: *(Enters carrying full egg box.)* Extraordinary people.

G: Ham! I forgot the ham.

B/A: Ham? Excellent.

D/C: Exactly.

E/F: Exotic.

B/G: Excruciatingly tasty.

All: *(Rest enter.)* Exeunt. *(Bow and exit together.)*

Maggie Norton

MYTHS AND LEGENDS

Scenario

Noah's Ark

Setting

The Flood.

Characters

Narrator; Noah; Noah's wife; Noah's three sons and their wives; pairs of animals; a raven; a dove.

Production notes

The following scenario is based on the story of Noah's Ark and can be used with five- to six-year-olds. The narration can be read by the teacher or told in his/her own words, appropriate to the age and experience of the class. The children can assume the various roles and mime the parts as indicated in italics. This can either be done in silence or to an accompaniment of taped or percussion music.

This story can be used several times, intensifying the drama as the children become familiar with it, inventing new ways to build the Ark, to show the animals approaching and to make sounds to accompany the action.

Narrator: A long time ago in a far away country there lived a good man called Noah. He had a wife and three sons, called Ham, Shem and Japhet. God was pleased with Noah and his family but angry with everyone else because they did wicked things. He spoke to Noah in a dream and said, 'I am going to punish the wicked people but I will save you and your family. Cut down trees and make a huge boat, an ark. It must be big, for in it you must take two of every bird, animal, insect and reptile. When you have finished I will make it rain for forty days and forty nights, till the water covers the whole earth.'

(The children mime cutting down trees, sawing planks, hammering in nails, carrying long pieces of wood in pairs, and carrying bundles of different weights and shapes, such as hay, bags of apples, boxes of nails and so on. Everyone helps to build the Ark. The shape of the Ark may be defined by ropes on the floor, or a more solid structure of chairs and tables.)

Noah and his family built a strong ark with many rooms inside it and when it was finished they went out into the forests and over the plains to find two of every animal – lions, tigers, mice, monkeys, rabbits, robins, spiders and crocodiles, in fact every creature on the earth. They brought them in to the Ark, two by two, and found food for them.

(The pairs of animals are found and brought in. The children become the creatures, miming the different movements and behaviour. Noah's family feed and settle them in the Ark.)

Then it began to rain. It rained and rained for forty days and forty nights. The water covered the grass and then the rocks and the trees, and at last even the hilltops were under the water. The Ark floated on the top of the waves and everyone inside it was safe.

(The class improvise the noises of rain, wind and thunder, and the movement of the Ark in the storm.)

At last the rain stopped and the water became calm. Noah looked out of the topmost window but all he could see was water. He sent a raven out of the ark. 'Fly over the waves and see if you can find land,' he said. But the raven came back. So he sent a dove. She at last came back bearing in her beak a piece of an olive branch so Noah knew that the flood was going down and that somewhere a tree was showing above the water. Soon the Ark felt a bumpety bump. It had come to rest on a mountain top and everyone could get out and stand once again on dry land. 'Look,' said Noah pointing to the sky. The Sun was shining and across the fading cloud was a rainbow. 'God is pleased with us. We must thank Him for saving us.'

(One child is sent off as the raven and another as the dove. The class should look astonished and happy as the rainbow appears. Everyone disembarks to celebrate deliverance from the flood.)

Barbara Roberts

Dramatic poems and dialogues

The legend of Philemon and Baucis

Setting

Ancient Greece.

Characters

Zeus; Hermes; Philemon; Baucis; Narrators or Chorus.

Scenery and props

A backdrop of a Grecian landscape painted by the children (optional); small branches of oak and lime; a staff; a table and chairs; a jug and pottery mugs or goblets.

Production notes

As this is a long piece, at least two narrators could be used or the narration could be presented in the form of a Greek-style chorus. In this way the narrative could be shared between several voices, for example, Group A (downstage right: voices 1, 2, 5, 6) say the first verse, Group B (downstage left: voices 3, 4, 7, 8) the second, and so on, except where specific characters are speaking. Named characters should speak their parts with the Chorus saying, for example, the words *'said Hermes'*. In such lines, the part of the chorus has been indicated in italics.

The actions can be entirely mimed, but a few simple props lend confidence to the actors. For high ground the four actors could stand on their chairs, Zeus and Hermes remaining on theirs till the end of the poem since they are gods, Philemon and Baucis stepping down as Philemon begins his plea, 'Then let us serve you...'.

The humorous mood of the poem changes in the last verses. This could be emphasised by the characters and chorus forming a tableau and holding their positions in silence for a moment after the last line.

Group A	**Voice 1:**	Zeus and Hermes came to Earth As travellers in need,
	Voice 2:	They found a green and pleasant land Which should have brought gods' speed.
Group B	**Voice 3:**	But when they knocked upon the doors To seek a slice of bread,
	Voice 4:	The people peered, then slammed them shut, 'Push off!' was all they said.
Group A	**Voice 5:**	*Said Zeus to Hermes,* 'This is bad, They're rich but all at odds, We'll punish them, we'll teach them it's No way to treat the gods.'

Group A **Voice 5:** *Hermes said,* 'You're right, all right,
The trouble is right now,
My human form's so hungry
I could eat a fatted cow.'

Group A **Voice 5:** They knocked on one last door for luck,
A humble little place,

Voice 6: A man in rags looked back at them,
A smile upon his face.

Philemon: 'Come in, come in, you're welcome here,
There's not a lot to eat,
But you must share in all we have
And rest your poor old feet.'

Group B **Voice 7:** It was a feast fit for the gods,
Well, gods in some distress,

Voice 8: They drank the cool refreshing wine,
While murmuring, 'God bless!'

Group A **Voice 1:** The couple who had served the wine,
Baucis and Philemon,

Voice 2: Grew puzzled, and a bit surprised
When not a drop had gone.

Group B **Voice 3:** They poured the wine into the cups,
The jug half empty stood,

Voice 4: But when they looked at it again,
The level was made good.

Group A **Voice 5:** 'Excuse me,' *Baucis blurted out,*
'Would it be rude to say,
We've known some wines, through many years,
But none's behaved this way.'

Voice 5: 'Fear not!' *cried Zeus,* 'My messenger
Who stands before your eyes,

Voice 5: Will tell you all.' 'Yes,' *Hermes said,*
'We're gods, but in disguise,

Voice 5: Now come with us, you pious pair.'
And on high ground they stood,

Voice 5: 'Behold,' *said Hermes,* 'What has happed
To those who were not good!'

GroupA **Voice 6:** Then Philemon and Baucis stared.
The land laid out below

Voice 7: Was flooded, every inch of it
(Zeus let his anger show.)

Group B **Voice 8:** 'Great gods,' *gasped Baucis,* 'Philemon,
Our home is safe and sound,

It's changed into a temple,
Where it stands is holy ground.'

Voice 8: 'Oh yes,' *said Zeus,* 'And you may choose
Whatever you desire,
For I will grant your every wish,
Or tell me I'm a liar.'

Philemon: 'Then let us serve you all our days,
Your holy temple keep.'

Baucis: 'And let us, when our day is done,
Together fall asleep.'

Group B **Voice 8:** And so it was, the god was true,

Group A **Voice 1:** They lived till very old
In happiness until the day

Voice 2: They found death was not cold;

Group B **Voice 3:** For when the moment came at last,

Voice 4: Great Zeus stretched out his hand

Group A **Voice 5:** And changed them both to guardian trees,

Voice 6: Exactly as he'd planned.

Group B **Voice 7:** Philemon became the oak,

Voice 8: And Baucis was a lime;

All: Together they stand side by side
Until the end of time.

Jenny Melmoth

Persephone

Setting

Ancient Greece.

Characters

Chorus; Persephone; Demeter; Hades; Zeus; Hermes; Charon.

Scenery and props

White sheets, draped Greek-fashion; masks for the Chorus, Hades, Zeus, Hermes and Charon; simple golden head-dress for Demeter; floral head-dress for Persephone; cloak for Hades; pole for Charon; confetti, silver foil, autumn leaves or paper; flowers; a pomegranate; green boughs.

Production notes

This piece for nine- to twelve-year-olds may be used as choral speaking. The parts may be organised as follows: Verse 1, everyone; Verse 2, three solo parts; Verse 3, everyone; Verse 4, first and second four lines solos, next nine lines group of girls; Verse 5, group of boys; Verse 6, group of girls; Verse 7, first four lines everyone, next eight lines group of boys; Verse 8, solo; Verse 9, first four lines everyone, each remaining line solos; Verse 10, everyone. The main characters should mime and do not speak. The actions and mimes are given in italics after each verse.

Long, long time ago
When all the world was new,
There lived and breathed Persephone,
In peace and love she grew.
Daughter of Demeter, Mother of the Earth,
A fair child of Olympus
Destined it seems from birth
To bring the gifts of joy and hope
To all who came her way,
A child of light and music
Who banished shadows grey.

(Chorus in three groups, some children holding autumn leaves and confetti or scraps of silver foil. Persephone enters from the right, giving out flowers and smiling. Demeter enters from the left and hugs her.)

Alas, alas Persephone,
She little knew her fate,
That grim, unyielding Hades
Would claim her for his mate;
That on a sunny summer's day
As meadows fair she'd roam,
A dark and handsome stranger
Would wrest her from her home,

To drag her to the Underworld,
Where walked the sightless dead.
To be his wife and sad-eyed Queen,
A privilege, he said.

(Persephone mimes picking flowers. Hades enters and after a brief struggle, drags Persephone behind the Chorus.)

Demeter, poor Demeter
In dread and frantic haste,
Searched vainly for her daughter
And soon the land lay waste.
The bronzed corn did wither
And trees did shed their leaves
Like myriad, amber falling tears,
So deeply did she grieve.

(Demeter searches for her daughter, people shake their heads, she weeps. Autumn leaves, confetti or silver foil are dropped as rain.)

For many years she roamed the Earth,
Her face a tragic mask,
Until she begged proud Zeus's help
To aid her in her task.
Hermes, swift on winged feet
He down to Hades sent
To bring back poor Persephone
If Hades would relent,
But her grim lord would keep her
If food of dead she ate,
And poor, unwise Persephone
Took upon her plate
A pomegranate, golden, round
It's flesh a crimson hue,
Juice and seven pips she had,
T'was only but a few
That sealed her fate forever...

(Zeus appears, Demeter falls on her knees, begging him to help her. Zeus summons Hermes and sends him to find Hades. Hades and Persephone appear from behind Chorus. She eats a pomegranate – seems to enjoy it, then suddenly realises what she has done.)

'Forever,' said grim Hades,
'For three months of the year,
You shall return to be my Queen
I shall await you here.
For all the other long months
To Demeter you may go,
But, harken, hasten back to me
When autumn breezes blow.'

(Hades points to Demeter, then to himself. Persephone kisses his hand.)

With what joy did Persephone
And Demeter meet again;
Spring burst out all around them,
Embracing them, the rain
Fell on an Earth awakened
To fertility anew,
To warmth and light and fruitfulness,
Such happiness it grew.

(Demeter and Persephone meet and embrace. Chorus hold up green boughs and drop confetti or silver foil. Hades beckons.)

Yet after Summer's finished
And harvest's gathered in,
Persephone must leave us
For Hades' caverns dim.
For Hades is a-calling
And Charon cannot wait,
The river laps his ghostly craft,
To travel is her fate
Deep down into relentless Earth,
Deep down to meet the dead,
To walk the winter long and hard,
By Hades' wishes led.

(Charon appears, pretending to punt a boat. Persephone steps into the boat. Back row of Chorus pull down their masks and enfold the couple.)

All things now die and wither.
The winter winds blow cold.
We grieve and mourn and shiver
At this tale we tell of old....
But, fear not gentle mortals,
Hark to the glad refrain,
'Persephone, Persephone',
For she will come again.
Provider of the sweet grass,
Provider of the grain,
Provider of the swaying corn,
Provider of the rain.

(Persephone slowly enters, the 'dead' push up their masks, everyone smiles. The other main characters join Persephone centre stage.)

For hope, it springs eternal
And everything's made new,
The world, its joys and sorrows,
A legacy for you.

(Everyone spreads their hands. On the last line, point to the audience.)

Doreen Towne

Scripted drama

Nowhere to go

Setting

Ninth-century Baghdad.

Characters

Hazrat Junaid, a Sufi teacher; the Fool, Junaid's favourite student; nineteen other students; market traders; customers.

Scenery and props

Tape of eastern music; white robe, Muslim prayer cap and prayer beads for Junaid; prayer mats; white robes, long dark coats and prayer beads for the students; a bucket; a broom; a bundle of wood; a flute; toy chickens.

Production notes

This is a play for a flexible cast number. It can be read or performed by a small group of children or a whole class group. It is based on a story from the life of the ninth-century Sufi saint, Hazrat Junaid. Depending on how much detail the teacher wishes to bring to the performance of the play, attention could be given to the designs of Islamic buildings, Islamic geometric and calligraphic patterns, Eastern furnishings and the nature, styles and role of religious music in Islam.

Scene 1

(It is early morning in Junaid's courtyard in Baghdad. The faint sound of gentle Eastern music can be heard in the background. Junaid is sitting at the front on a prayer mat with his eyes closed and is turning his prayer beads in his right hand. Sitting in two rows just behind him are sixteen students dressed like him in plain white robes. They appear to be praying but most of them are fidgeting as they sit. Some are yawning. Behind them are Eastern-style pillars. Another four students including the Fool, wander back and forth behind the pillars. They look busy with domestic duties. For instance, one walks across carrying a heavy bucket, another is sweeping the floor, a third walks past with a bundle of wood on his head.

After about a minute the music stops. Junaid opens his eyes and lifts his prayer beads to his lips. All the sitting students follow his example. The students then relax, some stretching their limbs. Junaid slowly gets up and brushes down his white robe.)

Junaid: *(Loudly.)* Is the water ready for my bath?

(The Fool hurries forward from behind the pillars.)

The Fool: *(Eagerly.)* Oh yes, Master. Everything is ready.

(He bends to pick up Junaid's prayer mat and folds it carefully. Junaid places his hand affectionately on the student's head.)

Junaid: Well done. You are a good lad.

(Junaid walks away behind the pillars and raising a curtain, goes into an inner room, followed by the Fool. The courtyard instantly buzzes with student chatter and activity. Some lounge about, others lean against the pillars, talking. Two are engaged in playful arm-wrestling. Another pulls out a flute and starts playing.)

Student one: *(Mimicking the student who has gone inside.)* 'Oh yes, Master. Everything is ready, Master.' Did you hear the Fool? Pah! He makes me sick!

(Everyone laughs.)

Student two: You are right. The Fool is always pleasing our teacher, but I can't imagine what Hazrat Junaid sees in him. In us he has nineteen of the best students anyone could ask for, and yet from the way he carries on you would think that the Fool was someone very dear and special.

(Several students nod their heads in agreement.)

Student three: That is so. We always listen to our teacher, show our respect to him for his great wisdom, and, without question, do everything that he asks of us. Every one of us is a much better student than the Fool. Yet Hazrat Junaid seems to be especially nice to him. It's most unfair.

Scene 2

(It is afternoon in Junaid's courtyard. Junaid is sitting on a raised platform and all twenty of his students are standing quietly, listening to him. They are all wearing long black or brown coats over their white robes.)

Junaid: I have called all of you this afternoon in order to set you a simple task. I want each of you to go to the market and buy a live chicken. When you have done this, return here and wait for my further instructions.

(The students bow to their teacher and at once set off for the market.)

Scene 3

(The students have arrived at the marketplace in Baghdad. They are noisily selecting chickens, haggling for them and chatting among themselves. In the background can be heard the sounds of a busy market and frequent chicken noises.)

Student four: I wonder why Hazrat Junaid has set us this task.

Student two: Perhaps we are going to raise chickens from now on. Then we can sell some of the eggs and keep some for ourselves.

Student three: That can't be. It would take up too much of our time which can be much better spent with our teacher. Most likely he is so pleased with our progress that he is going to hold a feast for us. If I am right, we will certainly have plenty of chicken to eat.

Student one: No, no. I don't agree. If we were going to have a feast, surely our teacher would not be wanting live chickens. Live chickens are not for eating.

Student two: What rubbish! Live chickens are just what one needs to be absolutely sure of their freshness for the feast.

Student five: Well, if you ask me, all of you are wrong. In my opinion Hazrat Junaid has sent us to do a meaningless task, just to test our obedience!

All Students: *(Shouting together.)* So who's asking you!

(In this way the nineteen noisy students each tries to impress their companions by showing that they understand what their teacher intends to do. Only the Fool makes no comment, but just does as he was asked.)

Scene 4

(The twenty students are standing quietly in Junaid's courtyard, each holding a live chicken – chicken noises could be simulated. Junaid is once again sitting on his raised platform.)

Junaid: Well done! Now I want all twenty of you to go away in different directions, each with your own chicken. Keep

going until you can hide your chicken in a place where no one can see you. Then come back to me.

(The nineteen students bow to Junaid and rush away. At the door they look back to see that the Fool is now sitting in the courtyard holding his chicken. They point at him and laugh loudly as they go out.)

Scene 5

(It is the same scene as the one before. Junaid and the Fool are sitting facing each other and meditating. There is a faint sound of gentle Eastern music in the background. Student one enters and is amused to see the Fool still sitting there with his bird, but bows to Junaid and sits down next to the Fool. Student two now enters and exactly the same actions take place. One by one all the students return and then sit down. The background music stops.)

Junaid: *(Looking at the Fool.)* Come forward and explain how it is that you are the only one who has not hidden your chicken.

(All the other nineteen students grin at each other in delight. One or two nudge each other and snigger. The Fool stands up and approaches Junaid.)

The Fool: Hazrat Junaid, you told us to go to a place where we could not be seen. Since Allah is everywhere and sees everything, there is no place where I cannot be seen. So there was nowhere to go and nowhere that I could hide the chicken.

Junaid: *(Smiling.)* Well done!

(Junaid stands up and immediately all the students rise. He looks sternly at them.)

Junaid: Are any of you left in any doubt now as to who is the best student? Need I say any more?

All nineteen students: *(Mumbling.)* No, Master.

(They hang down their heads in shame.)

Debjani Chatterjee

The golden touch

Setting

King Midas's garden; King Midas's palace and Dionysus's palace.

Characters

Narrator; Servant 1; Servant 2; Silenus, friend and old teacher of god Dionysus; King Midas; Dionysus; King Midas's daughter; courtiers and servants; musicians and dancers.

Scenery and props

Garlands of flowers; ivy chain; chair for throne; table and chairs; bowls; glasses; plates; apple; pillars; jug with bits of gold foil in it to represent gold water droplets; rose bush.

Production notes

This play, suitable for a class of nine- to twelve-year-olds, can be produced as elaborately as your resources allow. The different scenes can be indicated with painted backdrops or with free-standing scenery – such as a rose bush, pillar and so on. Torches covered with yellow cellophane can be shone on objects and people to indicate their turning to gold.

Scene 1

(King Midas's garden.)

Narrator: Once upon a time there was a rich king called Midas who ruled over the country of Phrygia. One day, two of his servants found Silenus, the famous story-teller and old friend and teacher of the god Dionysus, asleep in the famous rose garden of the palace.

Servant 1: Hey, old man, wake up! *(Shakes him roughly. Silenus moans.)* You have no right to be here.

Servant 2: You, stranger, on your feet! Drunk as a lord, the old dog! *(They pull him to his feet, propping him up.)* This is King Midas's garden, not a sty for pigs! *(Silenus staggers about trying to speak, but flops back to the ground.)*

Servant 1: Let's teach him a lesson. Help me tie him up with these. *(Laughing, they tie garlands of flowers round his wrists and hang an ivy chain round his neck, then pull him to his feet.)*

Silenus: W-what's going on? Y-you there! *(Holds out his bound wrists.)* Is this any way to treat a stranger? Take me to the king.

Servant 2: With pleasure, but the next time you feel like breaking into private property, don't try it here. This happens to be King Midas's rose garden, famous all over the world.

Servant 1: It's always well-guarded.

Silenus: You'll see. King Midas is a friend of my master, Dionysus. The King will be only too pleased to see me. *(Servants lead him off, laughing and mocking him with rude gestures.)*

Scene 2

(King Midas's palace.)

Silenus: *(Embracing King's knees.)* Your Majesty! Please, please be kind to a poor stranger who's lost his way.

Midas: And who are you? Why are you dressed up in this ridiculous fashion? *(Servants and courtiers giggle.)* Untie him immediately.

Silenus: Your Majesty, I am Silenus. And I'm very sorry for my strange appearance. I had a skinful or two of wine and in the midday heat... well, I suppose I must have fallen asleep in your beautiful rose garden. A thousand apologies. *(He bows low to the King.)*

Midas: Silenus? Not Dionysus's old friend and teacher?

Silenus: The very man, sir. *(Bows low.)*

Midas: Silenus, I'm so glad you've come to see us. *(To servants, who look astounded.)* Fetch the best food and wine. Spread a feast. *(To Silenus.)* You're our guest of honour. Sit here on my right. You can entertain us with some of your fabulous stories.

Silenus: *(Sitting by the King.)* Your Majesty, thank you very much for all your kind words.

Midas: You must excuse my men. They can be a bit rough. But, you know, we've had a lot of people trying to steal the roses.

Silenus: Let me congratulate you on having men with such a sense of humour. *(Bows to the King. Food and drink is laid out on a table before them.)*

Midas: *(Clapping hands.)* Bring in my musicians, and the dancers. My acrobats too. Silenus, we'll have the feast of a life-time.

Silenus: *(Bowing to the king and courtiers.)* Your wish is my command.

Narrator: So after several nights and days of feasting, entertainments and story-telling, King Midas decided to take Silenus back to his old friend, Dionysus, who had been looking for him everywhere.

Scene 3

(Dionysus's palace.)

Dionysus: Silenus! So there you are, you old rogue! *(Embraces him.)* I've been getting very worried about you. Oh, King Midas! *(Both bow to each other with a nod of the head.)*

Midas: Silenus took a little holiday with us, my lord. I'm sorry, it's our fault he stayed away so long. As you know, he has such a vast collection of wonderful stories to tell! We couldn't hear enough. He's quite worn out.

Dionysus: *(Embracing Silenus again.)* Midas, many thanks for bringing him back safe and sound. I must give you something in return. Just make a wish, and no matter what it is, it shall be yours.

Midas: *(Bowing slightly to Dionysus.)* Many thanks. Do you know, what I should most like to have is the golden touch which Silenus told us so much about in his stories. That must be a fabulous gift to have.

Dionysus: *(Shows concern.)* Are you sure that's what you really want? More than anything in the whole wide world?

Midas: After hearing some of Silenus's stories, I know that it is my dearest wish.

Dionysus: But you are already famous for being a rich king.

Midas: Yes, but I could be richer still, couldn't I?

Dionysus: Yes.

Midas: Anyway, it would be such fun. Just imagine, everything I touched turning to GOLD! I'll become a legend. An immortal. I shall be remembered for ever and ever!

Dionysus: So, you wish to become immortal? All right, but don't forget one thing.

Midas: What's that?

Dionysus: Your happiness and unhappiness must last for ever too. That's the way it is for us gods.

Midas: *(Not listening.)* It'll be magic! Sheer magic! I can't wait to get back to my palace. *(Claps his hands.)*

Dionysus: *(Sadly.)* All right then, the golden touch shall be yours once you return home. *(Shaking the King's hand.)* Goodbye and good luck, Midas.

Scene 4

(Back in King Midas's palace grounds. Midas is with his courtiers and servants.)

Midas: See here, everybody. *(Touches a branch of a rose bush; it turns to gold.)* Aren't I fantastic? *(Picks a rose which turns to gold in his hand.)* A golden rose, at last! Fabulous, whoever saw such a thing except in his dreams? *(Throws it into the air, catches it and throws it to a servant who throws it back.)* I wonder what it's worth? *(Throws it to courtiers who play ball with it between themselves.)*

Midas: *(Dancing round.)* What fun this is. Just wait till everybody hears about me.

Servant 1: You'll be world-famous, Your Majesty.

Servant 2: Even before the summer's over. *(Midas strolls about happily watching his courtiers play ball. He touches the pillar and watches it turn to gold.)*

Midas: Goodness gracious! By Zeus but Dionysus has rewarded me! I must be the only king in history who has a golden palace entrance. Oh, I must be the happiest man in the world.

Servant 2: How it all sparkles and shines, Your Majesty. A dream come true.

Servant 1: I can't believe my eyes. I wish I had such power. At this rate the whole palace will be turned to gold.

Scene 5

(King Midas's palace.)

Midas: Zeus, but I'm having fun! Oh, it's been such an exciting day. *(Claps.)* Bring in food and wine. The freshest bread and meat, fish, olives, apples, apricots, lemons and grapes. And only my best wine. We'll celebrate my new-found gift. Get a move on. But first let's have the coolest, freshest, water to wash off the day's dust. I shall be the most admired man of all time. *(Servant 2 pours water from jug over his hands. Water drops begin to turn to gold over his hands.)* Oh no! *(Laughs wildly; tosses golden droplets over shoulder.)* Never mind, only more for my treasure chests. A drink. I need some wine. *(Picks up a wine glass. As it touches his lips the wine also turns to gold.)* Ugh! What in the holy name of Zeus!

Servant 1: He'll go crazy.

Servant 2: And it's all so dazzling, so beautiful, so....

Servant 1: Useless! *(To King.)* Your Majesty, come, rest on your throne. You look worn out.

Midas: *(Flops on to throne which also turns to gold.)* This is some dirty trick. *(Gets up staggering about, touching different objects which all turn to gold. He swirls round and round before flopping to floor.)* Wait till I see that old dog Silenus again! He'll pay for this. *(Courtiers creep away to watch from the door.)*

Servant 1: Your majesty, remember, this was your heart's desire....

Midas: *(Gets up slowly to sit on throne again.)* So it was. Fetch me my darling daughter. She's always got a bright idea. She'll think of something. *(Servant 1 exits and enters immediately again with Daughter.)*

Daughter: Dearest Father, here I am.

Midas: My darling. *(Pulls her towards him and embraces her.)* Always so wise, so kind. Please, please help your old father... *(Midas's daughter now turns into gold like a statue.)* Oh no! No! NO! NO! NO! What have I done? I'm going mad. This is a nightmare.

Servant 2: Your Majesty, why don't you go back and see Dionysus? Tell him you were only joking. You didn't mean it.

Servant 1: Tell him you're sorry, for being so greedy.

Midas: All that once made me so happy is now only the death of me. Daughter, light of my life, can you ever forgive me? *(Begins to howl.)* Oh dearest one, why can't you look at me? Smile, speak to me, I beg you. How can I live without you? Yes, Dionysus did try to warn me. I wasn't listening. All I can do now is kill. I'm a murderer.

Dionysus: *(Appearing in doorway, laughing.)* Oh Midas, Midas, you who couldn't think straight for all your greedy stupid thoughts. Are you truly sorry?

Midas: Sorry? My lord, look at my daughter, a beautiful, cold, golden statue. Never again a kiss, a laugh or a wise word from her. I am the biggest fool on earth. *(Embraces Dionysus's knees.)* Please forgive me.

Dionysus: I see you are truly sorry and I will help. Go now and look for the source of the river Pactolus, near Mount Tmolus near the city of Sardis. Up there where the waters bubble into air, plunge in your head and body.

Midas: Of course, straight away. I'm off. Thank you, thank you. *(Bows to him and exits.)*

Narrator: So, King Midas set off alone to find the river Pactolus. There, at last, he washed more carefully than ever before in his life, ridding himself of the gift that had become a curse. His story has been told by generations of poets and if you ever go to the sands of the river Pactolus you can see for yourself how they glisten like gold in the sunlight.

Anna Taylor

The nectar of life

Setting

The world of Hindu gods and demons.

Characters

Indra, king of the gods; Bali, king of the demons; Vishnu, supergod who keeps the universe in order; Garuda, eagle; Turtle, Vishnu as a giant turtle; Mohini, Vishnu as a beautiful woman; Vasuki, king of the snakes (played by several children); Poison; Shiva, supergod who can make poison safe; gods; demons; three or four children to make a mountain.

Scenery and props

A cloak; a sash.

Production notes

This story comes from Hindu mythology. The children should be encouraged to use their imaginations to come up with ideas for portraying the more supernatural actions of the play. The mountains in the play can be made by three or four children joining hands to make a peak. Vishnu can ride Garuda by tying a sash to Garuda. Vasuki, the snake king, could be played by a number of children linked together in a chain, and Vishnu as the giant turtle can also be played by a group of children.

Scene 1

(The gods talk to Vishnu.)

1st God: Oh Vishnu, mightiest of gods, please help us! We're losing all our battles against the demons. They torment us day and night.

2nd God: If this goes on, they'll drive us out of heaven forever.

3rd God: Then what will become of us?

Indra: Please tell us what to do.

Vishnu: You must get the Nectar of Life. That is the only answer. It will be hard work. You must mix all different kinds of grasses, plants and herbs into the Ocean of Milk. Then you must churn the ocean with the biggest mountain you can find.

1st God: But... how can we move a mountain?

Vishnu: Get the demons to help you. But you must not take any of the things that come out of the ocean, or get angry if the demons snatch them.

2nd God: But what if they snatch the Nectar?

Vishnu: Do not worry. I promise you, because the demons are so cruel I will not let them have any of the Nectar.

(All exit.)

Scene 2

(The gods, led by Indra, talk to Bali and the demons.)

Indra: Oh mighty Bali, king of demons, we have a plan that will help all of us.

Bali: What plan could you have to interest me and my demons?

Indra: In the Ocean of Milk lies the Nectar of Life. Anyone who drinks the Nectar becomes very strong and never dies. If you help us, we can all share the Nectar.

Bali: Hmm! What do we have to do?

Indra: First we have to move the mountain and use it as a churn. If we get everybody together we can start straight away.

(All exit.)

Scene 3

(The children playing the mountain enter to centre stage and join raised hands to form a mountain peak. The gods and demons enter as if carrying tools on their shoulders. They dig carefully and slowly around the mountain and then put it on their backs to carry it away. This can be done by having each of the 'mountain' children ride 'piggy-back' on a god or demon. As the gods and demons work they repeat a rhyme.)

All: We're off to get the Nectar
Which will never let us die.
Come on friend and brother,
We can get it if we try.

    We know the work is harder
Than we thought it would be,
But we will get the Nectar,
Just you wait and see.

1st God: My back is killing me! I can't carry this mountain any further.

lst Demon: Whose idea was this anyway?

(The mountain starts to collapse on to the gods and demons.)

2nd God: Look out!

2nd Demon: Quick! Out of the way!

All: *(Shouting.)* Vishnu! Save us!

(The mountain collapses, crushing gods and demons – the children who are the mountain lie across those who were carrying them. Some gods and demons escape. Vishnu enters riding on Garuda. He blesses those under the mountain with a lifting wave of his right hand and they come back to life. Vishnu places the mountain – one of the children – on Garuda's back and they 'fly' to the seashore. All others follow. They put the child on Garuda's back down and the mountain reforms. Vishnu and Geruda exit. Vasuki the snake king appears.)

Vishnu: Ah, Vasuki! Let yourself be tied round the mountain like a rope. It won't hurt and you'll get a part of the Nectar.

(The gods and demons carry the mountain into the middle of the 'ocean' and wind Vasuki round it. The group who are Vasuki, kneel round the mountain and hold hands. Gods and demons stand on either side and mime pulling the 'snake' rope. Vasuki swings from side to side and the mountain does half turns in the middle. As they churn, they all chant.)

All: Churning, churning,
See the mountain turning.
We all know it's worth the strife,
We're out to get the Nectar of Life.

(Suddenly the mountain slips and sinks into the ocean – the 'mountain' children fall in a heap.)

3rd God: Oh no!

4th God: Now we'll never get the Nectar.

(Vishnu enters as a huge turtle – Vishnu in the centre as the 'head' can be surrounded by three or four children to make the body shape. The turtle 'dives' into the ocean and comes up with the mountain on his back. Everyone shouts with joy. The gods and demons wind Vasuki round the mountain again and start churning. The turtle helps. The churning throws up a dangerous Poison – a child with a cloak running in and out of the lines of gods and demons, who stagger and cry out in pain.)

1st Demon: Oh my eyes! I can't see!

2nd Demon: I can't breathe!

Scene 4

(The gods and demons run to Shiva, who is sitting cross-legged on the floor, meditating.)

Indra & Bali: Oh Shiva! Please save us from this deadly poison!

Shiva: Don't be afraid. I will make the poison safe.

(Shiva goes to the ocean with the gods and demons and draws the poison to him and makes it safe – the child with the cloak runs off stage.)

Scene 5

(Gods and demons churn the ocean with the mountain again, and chant. They see many beautiful and precious things come out of the ocean.)

All: Oh look, Oh look! What can you see?
Out of the waves – a beautiful tree.
Beneath the tree – a horse and a cow,
Here's the jar of Nectar now.

1st Demon: *(Mimes grabbing a jar.)* I've got it! I've got it! *(Dances with joy.)*

2nd Demon: Hey! You're not having all of it. I want some too.

Bali: Give me the jar. I'm your king. I shall drink first.

(The gods watch. Vishnu speaks to them while the demons quarrel.)

Vishnu: Don't worry. I'm pleased that you've kept your promise not to fight over the Nectar. The demons are already quarrelling. This has made them weak. Now I will charm them and give you the Nectar.

(Vishnu turns twice on the spot. There is a blackout and when light comes up again Vishnu has become the beautiful Mohini – another child.)

2nd Demon: Look at that beautiful woman!

3rd Demon: She's got the loveliest eyes I've ever seen!

Bali: Oh wonderful lady! Please share this jar of Nectar out between us. End our quarrelling!

(Bali mimes giving the jar to her.)

Mohini: Oh Bali, mighty Demon king,
Whose praises the three worlds sing,
I will do as you wish,
But only if you promise me this.
I will do things my own way,
My reasons though I will not say.
Stand on the shore in rows of two,
I will pour the Nectar for you.

(Gods and demons stand in two rows on the sea shore. Mohini mimes pouring Nectar into the hands of the gods.)

1st Demon: What's she doing? No, she can't do this to us. How dare she? Wait till I…. *(Starts to walk angrily towards Mohini.)*

2nd Demon: Shh! We promised. *(Pulling 1st Demon back by this arm.)*

3rd Demon: We can't argue with someone like her. She'd better not try anything funny, though. If she does, I'll….

2nd Demon: Oh, shut up. Be patient. You'll get nowhere like that.

(Mohini finishes the Nectar herself when she comes to the end of the row of gods. There is none for the demons. She spins round twice, there is a blackout and when lights come up Vishnu has returned in her place.)

2nd Demon: *(Very angry.)* It's Vishnu! He cheated us!

All demons: *(Very angry.)* Where's our share of the Nectar? Come on, we want our share of the Nectar.

Vishnu: You will never get the Nectar until you change your ways. Stop being cruel!

(Garuda enters. Vishnu 'flies' off as before with Garuda.)

Vinata Godbole

The innkeeper's tale

Setting

Bethlehem.

Characters

Narrator 1; Narrator 2; musicians; choir; Tobiah, an innkeeper; Mary; Joseph; Shepherds; three Wise Men.

Scenery and props

Biblical costumes; three decorated boxes for the Wise Men; musical instruments – recorders, chime bars, guitar, triangles, bongo-drums, piano and various percussion instruments.

Production notes

This musical narrative for Christmas can be performed by nine- to twelve-year-olds. The actors are required to mime and all the narration is performed by two readers and a choir. A group of musicians is also needed, and adult participation may be necessary in some cases. Instruments other than those specified could be used.

(Introductory music. Recorders and chime bars play 'The Corner Song' tune – see opposite. Chime bars play the last two bars as an introduction.)

Narrator 1: Tobiah, son of Levi, kept the inn at Bethlehem. It was uninviting, a mean place, and Tobiah was a mean man. He charged stiffly for the barest of hospitality and saved every penny for his own comfort and vanity.

It was, therefore, with great satisfaction that Tobiah heard the news of the Emperor's decree. Everyone was to be registered. All must return to their home towns. Visitors would crowd into Bethlehem and where would they stay? At the inn of Tobiah, son of Levi! His small black eyes glinted at the thought of all that extra business. He'd put his prices up and the cash would come rolling in!

Narrator 2: As the time of the registration drew near, travellers from everywhere came to fill the town. Some stayed with relatives or friends but many, rather than sleep rough, were forced to try for a room at the inn.

Tobiah was choosy. He could afford to turn away all but the most wealthy and this he did until, by one particular evening, he was fully booked.

Chuckling greedily, Tobiah went to lock up for the night. He peered out into the half-darkness. Latecomers still tramped wearily down into Bethlehem. He noticed two in particular – a young man and woman.

(Choir sings 'Christmas in Bethlehem', accompanied by guitar, triangles and bongo-drums. The guitar provides a two-bar introduction.)

Choir:

Calypso rythm

1. All through the hills so sand-y and still, a
Jo - seph and Ma - ry, wor - ried and wea - ry,

path___ comes wind - ing a - gain___ and again
press on to Christ - mas in Beth - le - hem.

2. The sky grows bright with thousands of lights,
As gentle evening draws in around them.
A few miles yet but the scene is set
It's almost Christmas in Bethlehem.

Narrator 1: Tobiah hesitated. The young woman was pregnant. She walked slowly, leaning on the man's arm. She would need somewhere comfortable – but that wasn't Tobiah's worry. Why get involved? He must look after himself! Besides, they didn't look rich enough for his liking.

He fumbled with the latch and hastened to go in, but the man had seen him and called out urgently, begging help for the woman. Tobiah's heavily lined face was forbidding and he shook his head firmly.

(Choir sings Verse 1 of 'The Corner Song', accompanied by recorders and chime bars. The chime bars play the last two bars as an introduction.)

Choir:

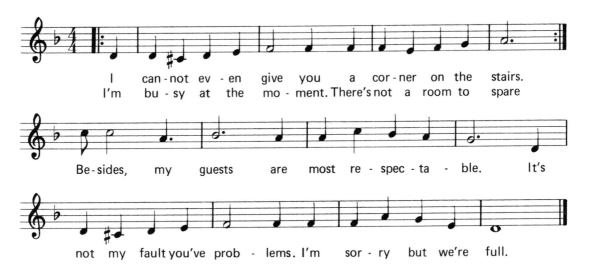

I can-not ev - en give you a cor-ner on the stairs.
I'm bu - sy at the mo - ment. There's not a room to spare

Be - sides, my guests are most re - spec - ta - ble. It's

not my fault you've prob - lems. I'm sor - ry but we're full.

Narrator 1: Feeling that he'd said enough, Tobiah tried to shut his door but the man blocked his way and pleaded with him.

(Choir sings Verse 2 of 'The Corner Song', accompanied by recorders and chime bars. The chime bars play the last two bars as an introduction.)

Choir: 2. If you could only give us a corner in your shed;
Now all we need is warmth and somewhere to make a bed.
The straw will do. It's very kind of you.
Our baby will be coming before the night is through.

Narrator 2:   The man's persistence began to annoy Tobiah. Yes, the best way to get rid of these unwanted guests was to let them bed down with the animals! They wouldn't put up with that for long! They'd be gone by morning. He took them out to the shed. They were surprisingly grateful. Muttering to himself about tramps and vagrants, Tobiah went back indoors.

(Recorders and chime bars play the last four bars of 'The Corner Song'.)

Narrator 1:   It was not until much later that there came a loud hammering on the door. Tobiah, already in his night-shirt, stumbled shouting downstairs. Who could this be now?

　　He raged even more when he found a bunch of ill-clad, unwashed shepherds crowding on to his doorstep. He would have sent them packing at once but they pushed round him, pouring out an astonishing tale. They claimed to have seen the sky ablaze and an angel who told them that the Messiah had come as a baby and was in a manger somewhere in Bethlehem. Tobiah didn't believe a word of it!

(Choir sings Verse 3 of 'Christmas in Bethlehem, accompanied by guitar, triangles and bongo drums. There is a two-bar introduction on guitar.)

Choir: 3. Such a disgrace, degrading my place,
Just common shepherds, the lowest of men.
What's in the skies? Despicable lies!
Don't give me your Christmas in Bethlehem.

Narrator 2:   But the shepherds were already making for his shed. Tobiah, bare-foot and shivering, went after them, catching at their rough woollen coats. He didn't want these sort of characters on his property. They'd disturb his animals, and you never knew what might be missing when they'd gone.

　　Shoving and arguing, Tobiah and the shepherds burst all at once into the rickety shed. Instantly, they were hushed by the cry of a new-born child. Tobiah stared. A dim lamp was burning and, by its light, he saw the travellers' baby, warmly wrapped, lying – in the manger!

　　That was what the shepherds had said! Could there be some truth in their story of angels? Was it possible that God's chosen one might come like this?

　　The shepherds were kneeling among the animals on the miry floor, worshipping the child. They talked for a while with the travellers, Joseph and Mary, and then they crept out. Tobiah immediately bustled out after them. Once in the street, the shepherds let their excitement flow out. They ran from house to house, waking everyone with their news.

(Choir sings Verse 4 of 'Christmas in Bethlehem' accompanied by guitar, triangles and bongo drums. There is a two-bar introduction on guitar.)

Choir: 4. Come through the streets; tell all that you meet
How God has smiled on his people again.
Messiah's come, salvation's begun.
Let's celebrate Christmas in Bethlehem.

Choir: *(Speaking in unison.)* Is it true? Is it really true? What's happening now?

(Choir sings 'Wise Men' with piano and percussion accompaniment. The piano plays the last two bars as an introduction.)

Jazz rythm

1. There's a buzz in the des - ert. There's a hum in the air.
The mi - ra - ges are shim - mer - ing. There's talk ever - y - where.
If you want to know what's go - ing down,
well, the three wise men are com - ing to town.

2. Listen out for those trumpets. Can you hear them all blow?
Now, look at those old camels. Do you see how they go?
Well, these ain't your us-ual Bedouin,
Come on, open up and show the men in.

Narrator 2: Right into the centre of the little town swept the entourage of three powerful eastern rulers. All thoughts of the tiny child drained from Tobiah's mind. He stood, comical in his night-shirt, and gaped. The great men themselves were gorgeously dressed, their robes of the rarest material, their heads and hands decked with priceless jewels. Even the saddles of the camels and the bridles of the pack-animals were richly embroidered. Curiously, the whole scene was brightly lit though the attendants carried no lamps.
The newcomers dismounted. Tobiah, son of Levi, wormed his way through the gathering crowd and grovelled before them. He begged them to reside at his humble inn and offered to throw out everyone who was already there!

Narrator 1: But the three rulers were gazing upwards. Tobiah now realised that the strange light was given by a star – a magnificent star whose increasing radiance spread out across the whole sky. It seemed to hang above Tobiah's inn – no, his shed! The rulers were nodding together. They turned to the bewildered innkeeper.

(Choir sings Verse 3 of 'Wise Men' with piano and percussion accompaniment. The piano plays the last two bars of the tune as an introduction.)

Choir: 3. We don't want any lux'ries; we don't want any fuss.
A star out in the far east has appeared unto us.
Now a king is born; that's what God said,
And we've found him here in your cattle shed!

Narrator 2: It was not that Tobiah *led* the three great men to his cattle-shed, rather he *followed* them in wonder, jostled by a throng of servants. His mouth opened wide when he saw the presents that they'd brought for the child. What treasures! Did they really think that this baby in the straw was a king?

Eventually, bowing very low, the eastern visitors withdrew. They paid little heed to Tobiah. He was left in the shed doorway to gaze after them till the last of their company had disappeared.

(The piano softly plays the last two bars of 'Wise Men'.)

Narrator 1: Tobiah sat down wearily on an upturned bucket in the corner of his shed. He considered the events of the day. Who were Joseph and Mary? More importantly, who was the child? Why did angels and a star announce his birth?

If this was God's Messiah, surely he, Tobiah, should have made him more welcome. Also, he should not have turned his nose up at the shepherds nor, on the other hand, grovelled to the eastern rulers. But he'd always been like that – putting himself first – never mind God nor anyone else. He felt wretched. God would surely punish him for his sins. How could he save himself?

Narrator 2: When Tobiah raised his head, he saw Joseph and Mary watching him. He went over to look at the baby, awake but peaceful. 'What's his name?' he asked, for something to say.

'Jesus,' was the reply. 'It means – "He shall save his people from their sins".'

(Choir sings Verse 3 of 'The Corner Song', accompanied by recorders and chime bars. The chime bars play the last two bars as an introduction.)

Choir: 3. I would not only give him a corner of my heart
But change my life entirely and make a second start,
For, even I, can see he is the one,
The saviour God has promised and prophets said would come.

(Recorders and chime bars play tune of 'The Corner Song.')

Anna Simon

MAKE - BELIEVE

Improvisations

These two improvisations are suitable for use with younger age groups.

Party guests

Setting

A grand ballroom.

Characters

Various well-known characters from fairy tales and nursery rhymes.

A number of famous characters from fairy tales and nursery rhymes have all been invited to the Mad Hatter's summer ball. How well do they all get on with each other? Does anyone misbehave? Who dances with whom?

Christina Dove

Robin Hood

Setting

Sherwood Forest.

Characters

Robin Hood; the Sheriff of Nottingham; Lord Blackstaff, a rich landowner; Lady Blackstaff; Vivienne, the Abbess; Lady Marian; Friar Tuck; Tom, a poor serf; Mary, Tom's wife; Blackstaff's guards; Robin's band of outlaws.

Production notes

A focus on appropriate behaviour other than fighting is necessary in this improvisation. A prior discussion would improve the role play.

Robin and his outlaws stop a party of travellers in Sherwood Forest. Robin declares that he is going to take from the rich and give to the poor. How might these travellers react? Whose side might the Abbess take? How could Marian and Friar Tuck help Robin, but not reveal themselves as his friends? Would Tom and Mary be able to accept Robin's help? Will the guards and outlaws risk their lives by fighting?

Alan Brown

Dramatic poems and dialogues

Dragon hunt

Production notes

This piece can be performed by any age group. The children should be led by a leader who offers mime and sounds for them to copy. Each phrase is followed by a mime or sound effect. Tell the children to yell 'Yes!' when you nod, and 'No!' when you shake your head. Most of the sounds are obvious, but here are some ideas for the rest:

- torch: click with tongue twice;
- along the trail: slap knees with hands like footsteps;
- grass: rub palms of hands together fast;
- hacking creepers: guttural 'ach' repeatedly;
- mud: very loud slow squelches, as if feet are stuck in it;
- uphill: hands slap knees, slower and slower as they reach top;
- downhill: ditto, faster and faster as they run down;
- resting: fast panting;
- shinning trees: 'chucka-chucka-chucka-chucka';
- telescope: hum on a 'V' to slide open and shut;
- swinging creepers: Tarzan yells;
- cave: repeat as if echoing, 'Cave-ave-ave-ave' and so on;
- dragon: huge roar from everyone, followed by screams.

Do you want to go on a dragon hunt? *YES!*
OK. Put on your haversack.
Put on your wellies... left... and right.
Put on your sword.
Check your torch is working.
Open the door
And away we go! Along the trail
Through the short grass,
Through the long grass,
Hack through the creepers!
Through the mud.
Have you seen any dragons yet? *NO!*
Along the trail,
Up the hill,
Rest at the top,
Down the other side.
Have you seen any dragons yet? *NO!*
Along the trail to the river,
Jump down the bank,
Dive in the river,
Swim to the other side.
Pull yourself out.
Rest.

Have you seen any dragons yet? *NO!*
Along the trail
Let's find a look-out – shin up a tree,
Open your telescope.
Look North! South! East! West!
Can you see any dragons yet? *NO!*
Close your telescope,
Swing down on this creeper.
Along the trail
Here's a cave.
It's dark in here.
Water dripping.
Listen! Can you hear something? *YES!*
Something breathing,
Something snoring,
Something scratching.
Reach out your hand.
It's warm.... It's slimy.... It's alive.... It's hungry....
It's waking up....
IT'S A DRAGON!

(Now, very fast indeed) Quick, quick!
Out of the cave-ave-ave – along the trail
Up the tree,
Swing down on the creeper.
Along the trail
Jump down the bank,
Swim to the other side,
Pull yourself out.
Up the hill,
Rest at the top,
Down the other side,
Along the trail,
Through the mud.
Hack through the creepers,
Through the long grass,
Through the short grass,
Slam the door!
Off with your left wellie!
Off with your right wellie!
Take off your sword
And rucksack
Phew! Have a rest!
Do you STILL want to go on a dragon hunt?
NO!

Christine Morton
(adapted from traditional African lion stories)

The Dark Avenger

Production notes

This poem for two voices can be performed by children aged eight and upwards. The voices belong to a child and a dog (indicated in italic type).

My dog is called The Dark Avenger
Hello, I'm Cuddles
She understands every word I say
Woof?
Last night I took her for a walk
Woof! Walkies! Let's go!
Cleverly, she kept three paces ahead
I dragged him along behind me
She paused at every danger, spying out the land
I stopped at every lamp-post
When the coast was clear, she sped on
I slipped my lead and ran away
Scenting danger, Avenger investigated
I found some fresh chip papers in the bushes
I followed, every sense alert
He blundered through the trees, shouting, 'Oy, Come 'ere!
   Where are you'
Something – maybe a sixth sense – told me to stop
He tripped over me in the dark
There was a pale menacing figure ahead of us
Then I saw the white Scottie from next door
Avenger sprang into battle, eager to defend her master
Never could stand terriers
They fought like tigers
We scrapped like dogs
Until the enemy was defeated
Till Scottie's owner pulled him off – spoil sport!
Avenger gave a victory salute
I rolled in the puddles
And came to check I was all right
I shook mud over him
'Stop it, you stupid dog!'
He congratulated me
Sometimes, even The Dark Avenger can go too far.
Woof!

Trevor Millum

Scripted drama

Rumpelstiltskin

Setting

A village in a faraway country.

Characters

Narrator; Miller; Marigold, the Miller's daughter; King; Rumpelstiltskin; Messenger; villagers; courtiers.

Scenery and props

A spinning wheel (make-believe); straw; gold (narrow strips of gold wrapping paper or wrapped coins); cradle; doll; two chairs; brooms.

Production notes

This play is suitable for a class of seven- to eight-year-olds.

Narrator: Once upon a time in a country far away there was a village where a poor Miller lived with his daughter.

(Marigold is playing with her friends – skipping, playing ball and so on. All activity stops as the excited Miller enters.)

Miller: Marigold! Marigold – where are you?

Marigold: I'm here, Father. Whatever's the matter?

Miller: It's the King! He's coming here! Well, don't just stand there.... Get this yard tidied up. Now! Hurry! *(Villagers rush off to collect brooms and start to sweep.)* And do take off that apron, Marigold. And put on some jewellery.

Marigold: But I've only got a necklace and a little ring.

Miller: Then go and get them. *(Marigold exits.)*

(Sound of horses' hooves off stage. King enters with courtiers. Villagers bow or curtsey. Miller bows several times, almost to the ground.)

Miller: What a great honour, Your Majesty. *(Bows again. Marigold enters, wearing necklace and ring.)* May I present my daughter, Marigold, Your Majesty. *(Marigold curtseys. The King smiles and takes her hand.)*

King: What a pretty name. *(A villager rushes forward with chair.)* Oh thank you. *(Mops his brow.)* It's such a hot day, isn't it?

All: Yes, Your Majesty.

King: Now, let's get down to business. *(To Miller.)* You know why I've come, don't you? *(Miller shakes his head. The King turns to villagers.)* I've come to collect your taxes.

All:	Taxes?
King:	Yes, you know. Cash. Money. Gold.
All:	Gold?
Miller:	Gold? But I don't have any gold. I'm only a poor miller.
King:	No gold at all? Not even one small coin? Not even one gold bar? *(Miller shakes his head.)*
Miller:	Alas, no.
King:	*(To courtiers.)* Right. Put him in irons. *(Courtiers grab the Miller who struggles.)*
Miller:	But Your Majesty.... *(Struggles again.)* Oh please....
King:	All right, let him speak.
Miller:	*(Who really has nothing to say.)* Er... er... well... er....
King:	Get on with it.
Miller:	Er... *(He looks at Marigold.)*...well, my daughter can turn straw into gold. *(Villagers react in surprise.)* With her spinning wheel.
Marigold:	But, Father....
Miller:	Don't interrupt, Marigold. Just give her a little time, Sire. That's all she needs. *(The King considers the idea.)*
King:	Oh, very well. But I'll be back, and there'll be trouble if you're not speaking the truth. *(He exits with courtiers.)*
Miller:	Quick! Get her spinning wheel. *(A villager fetches spinning wheel and stool.)*
Marigold:	But I don't know how. Why did you say such a thing? *(Villager hands her some straw, and the others crowd round to watch.)*
Miller:	You'll just have to try. Now come along everybody, she needs to be on her own. *(He exits with villagers. As he goes.)* Remember – we're all depending on you.
Marigold:	*(Studying the straw.)* But how do I start? I don't know what to do. *(Rumpelstiltskin, unseen by her, hobbles in.)*
Rumpel:	I know.
Marigold:	Who are you?
Rumpel:	Never mind that. It's so easy I could do it standing on my head.
Marigold:	You could turn this straw into gold?
Rumpel:	Nothing to it. Shall I show you?
Marigold:	Would you? Would you really?
Rumpel:	Only on three conditions.

Marigold:	Conditions?
Rumpel:	First, you must give me that necklace. *(Holds out his hand. She hesitates, then gives it to him.)* Then you must give me that ring. *(She reluctantly gives him the ring.)*
Marigold:	You said three conditions.
Rumpel:	So I did. When you're married to the King, you must give me the very first royal prince.
Marigold:	*(Laughing.)* Well, that's all right because I'll never be married to the King.
Rumpel:	So will you give me your word that I can have the prince?
Marigold:	Yes, all right. I promise.
Rumpel:	Right. Now give me that straw. *(He places the straw on the ground, and performs a small jumping dance around it.)* There. That's it. All done.
Marigold:	But it looks exactly the same.
Rumpel:	Of course it does. You'll find the gold over there. Don't you know *anything* about magic? *(He points and Marigold goes to a cupboard/desk and draws out a handful of golden strands/coins.)*
Marigold:	It's gold! It's real gold!
Rumpel:	I've kept my promise... now you must keep yours.
Marigold:	*(Suddenly doubtful.)* I don't know. Do I have to keep it?
Rumpel:	Of course you do. Unless....
Marigold:	Unless what?
Rumpel:	If you can guess my name, I'll release you from your promise.... Just guess my name, that's all. *(He exits.)*

(Miller and villagers return and discover the gold as King returns. General rejoicing and dancing in celebration as narrator continues.)

Narrator:	At the sight of the gold, all the village danced and sang until morning. *(King dances with Marigold.)* And the King was so happy that he asked Marigold if she would marry him. *(King drops to one knee. Marigold nods. They dance off, followed by the villagers.)* And as the years passed, Marigold forgot about the old man until one day, after the first young prince was born, she suddenly remembered her promise. *(A villager carries in cot. Miller, the King, Marigold and villagers enter. King is holding a long list.)*
King:	We've put down all the names we can think of. *(Reading.)* Tom, Dick, Harry....
Marigold:	I'm sure it won't be an ordinary name. *(Rumpelstiltskin enters, unnoticed. He stands listening.)*

King:	We mustn't give up. I've sent messengers out to every part of the kingdom. They're bound to find out what he's called. Meanwhile *(To villagers.)* Let's see what you lot can come up with. *(He points.)* You first.
First villager:	Cross eyes. *(King shakes his head.)*
Second:	Bandy legs.
Third:	Crookshanks.
Rumpel:	Useless! *(Everybody jumps, horrified.)*
Marigold:	You can't take our son!
King:	We shan't let him. Come on... names! Names! *(He points to each of the villagers who suggest a funny/unusual name. Each time Rumpelstiltskin shakes his head.)*
Rumpel:	You'll never guess it! *(He snatches the prince from cradle. Marigold rushes to grab him back, as a messenger, gasping, runs in to whisper something to her.)*
Marigold:	Are you sure? *(Messenger nods.)* Then tell everyone.
Messenger:	Your Majesty, I went to a great wood in the most distant part of your kingdom but I lost my way coming back and it has taken two whole days, but in that wood I saw him. *(Points to Rumpelstiltskin.)* He was dancing round a fire and he was singing.
Rumpel:	*(Interrupting.)* He's telling lies. Don't listen to him!
Messenger:	And what he sang was... *(Takes paper from pocket and reads. Rumpelstiltskin moves forward to snatch it but two villagers restrain him.)*
	'Merrily the feast I'll make. Today I'll brew, tomorrow bake. Merrily I'll dance and sing And to this place the new prince bring, I may be old, I may be lame But Rumpelstiltskin is my name.'
All:	Rumpelstiltskin? *(Furious, the old man shakes his fist.)*
King:	*(Laughing.)* Rumpelstiltskin. *(The villagers chase Rumpelstiltskin, shouting his name. He dodges them and runs away. King and Marigold stand holding the prince.)*
Narrator:	And that is why that village is now the happiest one in the whole kingdom, for the King said that because it had given him a wife and son who were more precious to him than gold, it need never pay taxes again. So, of course, everybody lived happily ever after, and Rumpelstiltskin was never seen or heard of again.

Kay McManus

Ling Soo and the Golden Bird

Setting

Ancient China.

Characters

Musicians; Narrator; villagers; Nobleman; Merchant; Golden Bird; Wang Chang, the Nobleman's nephew; Ling Soo, a little girl; sparrows; guards.

Scenery and props

Backdrop of village; traditional 'oriental' costumes; cardboard mask and wings for the golden bird and the sparrow.

Production notes

This play is suitable for seven- to eight-year-olds. It involves musical accompaniment from recorder or chime bar players and percussionists.

(Introductory music: recorders play 'Golden Bird' tune.)

Narrator: Our story is set in China. Here are the people of Nanchang village. *(Villagers come forward a little; bow to audience.)* Here is the old Nobleman who lives in the big house. *(Nobleman steps forward and bows to audience.)* The nobleman loves music but he cannot sing. *(Nobleman shakes head sadly.)* He is a good man and the people do not want to upset him. So they do not sing even though they can. They are all very unhappy. *(Villagers shake heads and begin to mime various forms of work.)*

(Enter Merchant, leading Golden Bird; walks up to Nobleman.)

Merchant: Would you like to buy this golden bird? Anyone who hears it sing will start singing too. *(Nobleman takes out money eagerly and buys Golden Bird. Exit Merchant.)*

Music: *(Recorders play 'Golden Bird' tune as Golden Bird glides in 'flying'. It dances and wends its way among villagers who stop to watch. When the tune has been played through once, everyone sings the 'Golden Bird' song.)*

All: The Golden Bird began to sing;
The Nobleman could hear.
He tried his voice and soon the notes
Were ringing strong and clear.
The villagers joined in as well
And every day that passed
Gave each of them a greater hope
That happiness would last.

(Golden Bird, Nobleman and villagers return to their places.)

Narrator: But, one day, the old Nobleman died. His nephew, Wang Chang, came to live in the house. *(Wang Chang steps forward looking grim; bows to audience.)* Wang Chang had no friends and he hated music. He did not want to sing.

(The 'Golden Bird' tune is played through once by recorders as Golden Bird 'flies' around behind Wang Chang. He turns angrily to see it.)

Wang Chang: Guards! *(Guards march to Wang Chang and stand to attention.)* Capture that bird! I don't want to hear the villagers sing. *(Guards catch Golden Bird. It drops three feathers. Guards take Golden Bird away to side of stage. It cowers there. Guards stand in front of Golden Bird linking arms as if imprisoning it. Wang Chang exits.)*

Narrator: The guards put the golden bird in a cage. All that was left behind were three golden feathers. Ling Soo found them. *(Ling Soo picks feathers up and gazes at them sadly.)*

Ling Soo: Poor bird. I WISH I knew where it was. *(Tinkling of bells. Sparrows dance to sound of bells, encircling Ling Soo. Sparrows stop dancing and point towards place where Golden Bird is being held. Everyone sings the 'Golden Bird' song to a recorder accompaniment.)*

All: Each feather that was left behind
Will grant a wish, Ling Soo.
You wished to find the Golden Bird
And now that will come true.

(Sparrows return to places. Ling Soo creeps cautiously towards guards. They un-link arms and spring forward with 'swords' drawn. Ling Soo jumps back in fright.)

Guard 1: You must not come near the Golden Bird.

Guard 2: It is here by order of Wang Chang.

Guard 3: Go or you will die!

(Ling Soo holds up a golden feather.)

Ling Soo: I WISH you guards were fast asleep! *(Sound of tinkling bells as guards yawn, stretch and gradually fall asleep. Bells stop. Golden Bird rises from its cowering position and steps over guards. Ling Soo takes its 'wing' happily. Villagers come forward a little, as do the sparrows.)*

Villagers: *(Speaking in unison.)* The Golden Bird! Ling Soo has found the Golden Bird!

(Wang Chang suddenly appears, pushing through the villagers towards Ling Soo and the Golden Bird, brandishing a 'sword'.)

Wang Chang: Oh no you don't! I will lock you in my deepest dungeon!

Villagers: *(Speaking in unison, urgently.)* The last feather!

Ling Soo: *(Holding up a feather.)* I WISH Wang Chang was a kind man who loved to sing!

(Sound of tinkling bells. Wang Chang throws 'sword' aside and smiles. Bells stop and Wang Chang sings a few notes. He laughs in delight and throws his arms round Ling Soo.)

Narrator: Then the Golden Bird flew over the village singing its magic song. *(Golden Bird 'flies' back and forth across the stage, finishing on the opposite side to narrator. Guards stand up. Old Nobleman, Merchant and sparrows return.)* Soon the villagers and Wang Chang are singing too.

(Everyone sings the 'Golden Bird' tune, accompanied by recorders.)

All: Ling Soo has found the Golden Bird;
Wang Chang's a happy man.
In Nanchang we will sing
As often as we can!

(Tinkling of bells as all take bow.)

Anna Simon

Small wonder

Setting

A town square.

Characters

Merryweather, a toymaker; Maggie, a little girl; Joe
Spry; Mrs Potter; townsfolk; Mrs Potter's dog; the
Mayor; the Queen; the Queen's messengers.

Scenery and props

Hobby horse; pyjamas, robes and chain for the Mayor; a crown and robes
for the Queen; a large model bird painted silver; a conker still in its case;
sound effects for horse's hooves, cuckoo clock and trumpet sound.

Production notes

This play for seven- to eight-year-olds involves considerable preparation
in terms of costume and sound effects. The children should be allowed to
contribute to this as far as possible.

Scene 1

(Sound of coconut shell hooves – and possiby a trumpet.)

Merryweather:	Who's this coming in such a hurry? *(Enter Queen's messenger, almost knocking over Merryweather.)*
Messenger:	You fellow, which way is the Mayor's house?
Merryweather:	It's over there, in front of you.
Messenger:	Then out of my way! Out of my way! This is important! Very important!
Merryweather:	Well! Very important? Very rude more like it! *(Exit.)*

(Messenger knocks impatiently on the door of the Mayor's house.)

Messenger:	Come on, come on. Open up. This is important. *(Mayor, in nightclothes and chain, appears.)*
Mayor:	What d'you want at this time of the morning? I haven't had my breakfast yet.
Messenger:	Bother breakfast. This is really important....

Scene 2

(Mayor and Queen's messenger in town square with townspeople.)

Mayor:	People of this town, I have called you here this morning because we have a very important visitor.
Messenger:	I am a royal messenger. I come directly from the Queen.
Mayor:	D'you hear that everybody? Directly from the Queen herself!

Messenger:	I bring a royal proclamation.
Mayor:	Imagine that! A royal proclamation.
Messenger:	Oh shut up, you unimportant little man. 'Hear ye, people of this town, this royal proclamation. The Queen is bored – bored with the gold and silver stacked in her counting house, bored with the priceless jewels that sparkle in her crown, bored with the grovelling of courtiers at her royal feet. People of this town, the Queen is thoroughly bored with everything. Therefore, she has decided to process through every town and village in her kingdom seeking a great new wonder, something entirely new that has never before been seen by human eyes. Glory and wealth will be given to the person who can show Her Majesty such a wonder. People of this town, prepare yourselves: the Queen arrives here in two days.' That is my proclamation. I now depart. I have important business. *(Mounts horse.)* Out of my way! *(Exit. Coconut hooves.)*
Mayor:	Goodbye! Thank you for coming! We're very honoured! Very, very honoured! Very, very, very honoured! Bye! *(Departing hooves.)* He's gone. People of this town, this is unbelievable. The Queen is coming here! Yes, actually coming here in all her royal importance! She's going to give us glory and wealth. She'll make me a knight, I'll be Sir Mayor, no she won't she'll make me a duke. I'll live in a grand house with lots of pillars and marble steps and footmen and servants....
Joe:	Hang on a minute, Mr Mayor. Haven't you forgotten something?
Mayor:	Forgotten something? Oh yes, the golden coach! I'll drive around in a golden coach....
Joe:	No, no, no. First things first, Mr Mayor. And the first thing is: we've got to find a great new wonder never before seen by human eyes.
Mayor:	Oh yes... yes, of course. Right then. Listen carefully everybody. I want some ideas from all of you. I'll be here in the market square. I want you all to bring me, and this is important, your cans for the plunder.
Joe:	Don't you mean your plans for the wonder?
Mayor:	That's exactly what I said!

Scene 3

Mayor:	I've been waiting here all morning. I've seen half the town and not one of them has had a good idea. Oh, I deserve better than this. Next!
Mrs Potter:	*(Carrying a parcel.)* Morning Mr Mayor. I've just been

	home and got my wonder. I'm sure it's what we're looking for. Now then. There. *(Unwraps a jug.)* What d'you think about that then eh?
Mayor:	It seems to be a milk jug....
Mrs Potter:	A gravy boat actually....
Mayor:	In the shape of the Queen's head.... And?
Mrs Potter:	Well it's most unusual, en it? And I thought the Queen would like it, what with it being her head.
Mayor:	Mrs Potter, the Queen is looking for a great new wonder never before seen by human eyes. I can't give her a cracked gravy boat, you ninny-headed old nincompoop.
Mrs Potter:	Oh... so it's no good then?
Mayor:	No good? No good! Of course it's no good. Next! *(Exit Mrs Potter.)*
Joe:	Morning, Mr Mayor. I've got a real wonder here all right.
Mayor:	Well, what is it?
Joe:	Let me tell you. I were down on the beach one midnight digging for lugworm. It were a full moon, the light shimmering on the waters, the waves rolling and ebbing, rolling and ebbing, rolling and ebbing....
Mayor:	Yes, yes get on with it.
Joe:	I'd got half a jar of lugworms when suddenly I heard this eerie supernatural melody, and sitting there on a rock was a mermaid, combing her hair and singing to the moon. Well! Can you imagine my surprise?
Mayor:	Yes, yes, I can. Just get on with it.
Joe:	Well, I put down me jar of lugworm, crept up behind her, grabbed her tail and held on for dear life. Then she wriggled and wriggled, shook herself free and plunged into the sea – leaving me holding her tail. A real mermaid's tail. There. *(Shows Mayor a large fish tail.)* What d'you think then eh?
Mayor:	Mm... very fishy. This looks like the tail of a large haddock to me. And your whole story sounds like a load of codswallop.
Joe:	Oh, so it's no good then?
Mayor:	Of course it's no good, you stupid boy. Next! Oh no, not you, Mrs Potter.
Mrs Potter:	Yes, I'm back again, Mr Mayor. I've been home, I've thought about it, and this time I bring with me a real wonder. Fit for a Queen, no doubt about it.
Mayor:	What is it then?

Mrs Potter:	My dog.
Mayor:	That mangey old mongrel there. What's so wonderful about it?
Mrs Potter:	It can talk.
Mayor:	Talk?
Mrs Potter:	As well as you or me. As good as any human can. That dog is our fortune. The Queen will be astonished.
Mayor:	Well, let's hear it then.
Mrs Potter:	Now then, dog, say, 'Humpty Dumpty sat on a wall'.
Dog:	Woof, woof, woof.
Mrs Potter:	Good dog. Now say, 'I'm pleased to meet you, Your Majesty.'
Dog:	Woof, woof, woof.
Mayor:	It's not talking. It's just barking. It's just going, 'woof, woof, woof' the whole time. It's not talking.
Mrs Potter:	It is. It's talking. As good as any human being. It's just your ears aren't tuned in enough. But the Queen will hear it all right. She's got royal ears.
Mayor:	Next!
Dog:	Woof, woof, woof.
Mrs Potter:	He says, 'Please Mr Mayor give me a chance.'
Mayor:	Next!
Mrs Potter:	Come on, dog. At least I understand what you're saying.
Mayor:	Next!
Maggie:	Good morning, Mr Mayor!
Mayor:	Oh go away. I'm busy. I'm trying to find a great new wonder. I've got no time to talk to children. Next!
Maggie:	But, Mr Mayor, that's what I've come about – the wonder for the Queen.
Mayor:	Oh don't tell me – you've got something at home that is absolutely guaranteed to astonish the Queen. A cracked gravy boat perhaps, or a talking dog, or a mermaid's tail.
Maggie:	No Mr Mayor, I haven't got anything – but there's someone in the town who could make something so wonderful that it's bound to astonish the Queen.
Mayor:	Who?
Maggie:	Well... who's the cleverest person in the town?
Mayor:	I am.

Maggie: Oh... well who's the cleverest and kindest person in the town?

Mayor: I am!! But I don't see where all this is getting us.

Maggie: Well, actually Mr Mayor, I wasn't actually thinking of you. I was actually thinking of Mr Merryweather.

Mayor: Merryweather! That old crackpot. That wretched cuckoo clock of his kept me up half the night. *(Cuckoo clock cuckoos.)* Be quiet!

Maggie: But Mr Mayor, we're the only town in the whole of the land with a town hall cuckoo clock. He's the cleverest man, Mr Merryweather. He makes monkeys that climb up sticks, and ships that sail in bottles, and little horses that walk along, and birds that flap their wings. I'm sure he could make a wonder for the Queen.

Mayor: Oh very well. It's worth a try. We haven't got any other ideas. *(Exit Maggie.)* Merryweather! Oh I deserve to be Mayor of a cleverer town than this. It seems like my best hope of being made a knight depends on old Merryweather. *(Enter Maggie with Merryweather.)*

Maggie: Come on, Mr Merryweather. I'm sure you can do it.

Mayor: Ah, Merryweather. Now then, you know of course that the Queen is coming to town in two days time?

Merryweather: Ar, I've heard something about it.

Mayor: Heard something about it? I should hope you have. It's the most important thing that's ever happened to this town. And you know that the Queen is looking for a great new wonder that's never before been seen by human eyes?

Merryweather: Ar, I've heard that as well.

Mayor: Well, I've had a very good idea. I've decided that you shall have the honour of making the wonder. It's got to be wonderful, mind. And never before seen by human eyes. A lot depends on this you know. I'll be made a knight, or perhaps even a duke. Any questions?

Merryweather: How long have I got?

Mayor: Two days.

Merryweather: I'll see what I can do.

Scene 4

(Two days later.)

Mayor: This is it! The big day! The day the Queen is coming! The greatest day of my life! Do I look important? Is my hat on straight? Mrs Potter's wretched dog chewed it half to pieces. I just hope Merryweather's worked up a wonder, that's all. I can't make head nor tail of that man. My speech! I must remember my speech! 'Your Majestic Queenliness, it is with....'

Mrs Potter: She's coming! She's coming! *(Crosses the stage, with dog barking.)*

(Enter Joe. Blows a ragged fanfare. Exit. Enter Queen and her messenger.)

Messenger: People of this town, never has such an important thing happened to you! The Queen has come! She seeks a great new wonder, never before seen by human eyes. People of this town, have you a wonder to bring before Her Majesty?

Mayor: Your Majestic Queenliness, it is with the most postponed palitating and polymorphous pleasure that I....

Messenger: Yes, yes, the Queen thanks you and wants to see the wonder.

Mayor: ...That I, this town's mighty, marvellous, mellifluous Mayor extends to you a warm and weltering....

Queen: Oh be quiet, you boring little man. Have you got a wonder or not?

Mayor: Er... yes, Your Majestic Queenliness. Bring out the wonder!

(Fanfare. Merryweather brings out a marvellous metal bird.)

Merryweather: We bid you welcome to this town, Your Royal Highness.
Even though, Your Majesty, you are a royal queen
I'll make bold to claim you've never seen
A bird like this before –
Not in a gilded courtly cage, nor
Flying free across a moor.
Listen, Your Majesty, for my metal bird has song.
Like any bird, it sings in praise
Of peaceful nights and ordinary days.

Now see, Your Majesty, the motion of its wings.
At first it flaps as helpless as a fledgling,
But then, as young ones do, it learns,
Finds skill, grows wise;
Now watch it rise
Above your royal head. It flies!

Queen: Oh splendid! Splendid! I've never seen the like in all my royal days. Mr Merryweather, what a clever, ingenious, inventive man you are!

Merryweather: But if I might, Your Majesty, be so bold to mention,

This is a mere mechanical toy to gain your royal
    attention.
The real wonder lies within.
This bird of iron has no heart.
Instead inside its breast
Rests a red cushion
An on that cushion lies
A new wonder, never before seen on earth by human
    eyes!
Your Majesty
Put in your royal hand and see.

Queen: It's a conker. A spikey green conker! I am a Queen. And this is a conker.

Mayor: Your Majestic Queenliness, I really can't apologise enough. Merryweather, you blithering nincompoop, and things were going so well!

Merryweather: Your Majesty must understand
What you're holding in your hand.
Split open its green spikey skin,
Inside a bright new conker lies –
A wonder never seen before
On earth by human eyes.

(Ominous pause. Then Queen laughs with delight.)

Queen: Mr Merryweather, not only are you the most clever and ingenious inventor, you are also a grand philosopher! *(Cuckoo clock cuckoos.)* Your cuckoo, I see, agrees. You must be my royal inventor.

Merryweather: Your Majesty's most kind, but this is where I live,
And I've jobs of my own that I want to get on with.

Queen: Very well, Mr Merryweather. It seems that, not only are you a clever inventor and a grand philosopher, you are also a very independent man.

Mayor: Oh most magnificent Majestic Queenliness, as Mayor of this town, and bearing in mind the great success of today's proceedings, would it be possible to have a knighthood now?

Queen: A knighthood? A knighthood! Oh Mr Mayor, a knighthood is but a worthless trifle. I'll give you something far more valuable.

Mayor: Oh your Majestic Queenliness, you mean a dukedom?

Queen: No, Mr Mayor, I mean this conker!

Tony Jones

The babes in the wood

Setting

The Needy family's cottage; a forest and a witch's cottage.

Characters

Mr Needy; Mrs Needy; Joan, their daughter; Mark, their son; Rover, the dog; Robin Hood; Maid Marian; Witch; Cat Boy.

Scenery and props

Backdrops for a humble cottage, a forest and a Witch's cottage; costumes for all cast; table; chair; large box; large book; items for the Witch's cottage such as a cauldron and a broomstick; garden gnome or similar ornament.

Production notes

This is a traditional pantomime for nine- to twelve-year-olds. Fairly elaborate scenery, props and costumes are needed for it and the children should help to devise these where possible. They should also try to work out the best way of showing the transformation of the Cat Boy in Scene 5.

Scene 1

(The Needys' cottage one evening.)

Rover: *(To audience.)* You all will recognise that I'm
A talking dog in pantomime.
These two don't hear my wise remarks,
All they expect from me are barks.

Mrs Needy: My dear, how are we going to live?
I've neither crust nor crumb to give
Our children. We've no cash to spend.
What can we do? Is this the end?

Rover: *(To audience.)* She's right. It's bad. An empty purse.
But listen now. Things get much worse.

Mr Needy: I hate to see them weak and thin.
Tomorrow it will be no sin
To lead and lose them in the wood.
That way we may do them some good.

Mrs Needy: Some good! You're mad! How will they fare?
The prey of night-time wolf and bear!

Mr Needy: Enough! Trust me. We go by day
And leave them by the broad highway
And then some kind and wealthy man
Will come, according to my plan,
And find them there and, touched by pity,
Will take them with him to the city.

Mrs Needy: But will that work? I've never thought
That many rich men were that sort.

Mr Needy: You'll see. Well fed and by his fire
He'll give them all their heart's desire.

Mrs Needy: But what if no one travels by?
They'll spend all night beneath the sky.

Mr Needy: Oh, no, they won't. Should evil roam,
As darkness falls, I'll bring them home.

Rover: *(To audience.)* This scheme's no good, as you have guessed.
Those children will be most distressed.

Scene 2

(Mark and Joan stand by the broad highway in the forest.)

Mark: Now where is Dad? He's very late.

Joan: He said we'd got to stand and wait.

Mark: We've been here hours and no one's come.

Joan: We'll never find our own way home.

Mark: We need to shelter.

Joan: Where d'you think that track will lead us?

Mark: To some kind soul who'll warm and feed us?

Joan: It might. There's nothing else in sight.

Mark: You're right. Yes. Things don't look too bright.

Joan: We can't just stand and get soaked through.

Mark: Come on. There's nothing else to do.

(They take the path into the dark wood.)

Scene 3

(The Needys' cottage again. There is a knock at the door.)

Mr Needy: A visitor? Who can that be?

Mrs Needy: Now why ask me? Just go and see.

Mr Needy: *(Opens door.)* Maid Marian and Robin Hood!
What have you brought us? Money? Food?

Mrs Needy: Welcome, good friends, who help the needy
By stealing from the rich and greedy!

Maid Marian: Unluckily, we can no more
Dish out our stuff among the poor.
An evil witch, who's come to stay
Our gold and gems has charmed away.

Mrs Needy: A wicked witch? With spells and magic?
Here in these woods? Oh, this is tragic!

Robin Hood: I understand your consternation
But what we need is information.

Maid Marian: She settled here not long ago
To prey on children. That we know.

Robin Hood: Have you seen any sign or trace
Which might reveal her hiding place?

Mr Needy: I've walked this wood from end to end
And seen no witches here, my friend.

Maid Marian: Her house enchanted then must lie
Invisible to human eye.

Robin Hood: Except to children who, I fear
Are drawn to it and disappear.

Mrs Needy: Henry, you fool, our Mark and Joan
Are out there wand'ring all alone!
Defenceless as the night comes on!

Mr Needy: Don't make a fuss. If they're in trouble,
I'll nip and find them at the double.

Robin Hood: Children out there! Things do look black!

Mr Needy: You just stay here. They may come back.

Mrs Needy: I can't sit here! I'll come with you.

Mr Needy: You'll do just what I tell you to.

Robin Hood: Enough! Now cease this petty strife!

Rover: *(To audience.)* Well said. We've had enough of nattering
And wasting time in idle chattering.
These two will drive me to distraction!
So – no more words. It's time for action! *(Exit Rover.)*

Robin Hood: We must move fast. The Witch's power
Grows with the darkness hour by hour.

Maid Marian: It's luck we need. The Merry Men
Have hunted for the Witch's den
Through bush and brier by night and day
Without success. No signs betray
Her hiding place.

Robin Hood: We must away
And find those two before harsh fate
Befalls them and we come too late.

Scene 4

(Mark and Joan in the wood.)

Joan: I'm cold and wet and hungry, Mark.

Mark: Me, too, and it's so blooming dark.

Joan:	We'll have to keep on through the night.
Mark:	Oh no, we won't. Look. There's a light.

(Cat Boy comes through trees with a lantern. Rover appears behind tree.)

Rover:	*(To audience.)* A lantern and a large black cat? I don't much like the look of that.
Cat Boy:	You needn't stand out here and freeze There's shelter for you through those trees.
Joan:	How suddenly that house appeared From nowhere. And it does look weird.
Rover:	*(To audience.)* The Witch's place! Just as I feared.
Cat Boy:	Yes. Burning blue its windows glow. My mistress lives there and we know Your story. Come. Don't be afraid. We've sandwiches and lemonade.
Mark:	I haven't had a cake for years.
Cat Boy:	Poor boy. Then come and have no fears.
Rover:	*(To audience.)* There's dirty work afoot, I'd say Good job that I'm not far away.

(He follows Cat Boy and the children.)

Scene 5

(Inside the Witch's house. Cat Boy and the children enter.)

Witch:	At last you're here. Cat – you did well. *(Aside.)* And now to work my little spell. *(To them.)* Sit down. Get warm. Don't hesitate. The table's ready. Take a plate.
Mark:	Cream cakes and drinks and all for us?
Joan:	Ham sandwiches. How generous!
Witch:	And sausages and rich jam tarts! *(Aside.)* Enchanted by my evil arts. I hate all children and I cast My spells to hold and keep them fast.
Cat Boy:	*(Aside.)* It's true. She's sly and cold and vicious!
Mark:	These cream cakes really are delicious.
Joan:	I've never had such splendid stuff.
Mark:	I really think I've had enough.
Witch:	More than enough. And now you stand Obedient to my command.
Mark:	What's this? I just can't stir a limb.
Joan:	And I can't, either. This is grim.

Witch:	Aha! You cannot lie or sit Or walk until I order it. Now, Cat! Roll out the magic chest.
Rover:	*(Enters.)* Is that the way to treat a guest?
Cat Boy:	A dog!
Witch:	A talking dog.
Rover:	Surprised?
Joan:	Rover! I never realised That you could talk.
Rover:	I keep it quiet.
Witch:	Some magic food?
Rover:	I'm on a diet.
Witch:	No matter. You can't interfere.
Cat Boy:	*(Bringing chest.)* Your chest and magic book are here.
Rover:	You're into witching – that I've guessed. I must say I am most impressed.
Witch:	At my command each child will climb Into the chest and magic rhyme Will turn them into gnomes of plastic.
Rover:	Is that right? Sounds quite fantastic. Why gnomes?
Witch:	Why not? You try my patience. They sell as garden decorations. And you, you nosy, cheeky dog, I'll turn into a plastic frog.
Rover:	I bet you can't. A chest that small Won't hold those kids. They're far too tall.
Witch:	That chest, as any fool can see, Will hold someone the size of me.
Rover:	It won't.
Witch:	You're dense; A dog without intelligence. Look. In I climb and here I sit With ample room. A perfect fit!
Rover:	*(Closes lid.)* I shove her down in the magic box And slam the lid, make sure it locks. Then from this book I read the charm: 'Dark spirits here of hurt and harm, Allagazam! At my behest, Perform your task within the chest!'
Joan:	You've saved us Rover!

Mark: What a stroke!

Rover: I bet the Witch won't see the joke.
I lift the lid and so present
No Witch but a garden ornament. *(Takes out a gnome.)*

Joan: And will she always stay that way?

Rover: Until the spell wears off, I'd say.
Now all her wicked sorcery
Is gone and everyone's set free.

Cat Boy: *(Changes into a boy.)* Her gnomes are children once again,
As I my normal shape regain.
Cat I am not and here you meet a
Happy boy whose name is Peter.
My father is Lord Wealthy, who'd
Be glad to show his gratitude
By heaping open-handedly
Much gold on those who set me free.

(Robin Hood, Maid Marian and Mr and Mrs Needy enter.)

Robin Hood: As we passed by, to our surprise
The house appeared before our eyes.

Peter/Cat: Quite so. The binding spell is said
And all the Witch's power is dead.

Mr Needy: Praise be! Are you two kids all right?

Joan: We are. But we've had quite a night.

Mrs Needy: Don't worry. We'll soon have you home.

Maid Marian: Whose is that hideous garden gnome?

Peter/Cat: Before we start the explanations
I have further revelations.
Inside this cupboard *(Opens it.)*, piled up high
Are bags of gold and jewellery.

Robin Hood: Gathered up by magic art
And here through witchcraft set apart.

Maid Marian: And so, from witchcraft free, the wood
Gives money for all poor folks' food.

Rover: *(To the audience.)* Thus Peter goes home to Lord Wealthy
Who, glad to find him safe and healthy,
Will make the Needys' life less hard
By paying out a large reward.
And Robin and his men, once more,
Can do good work among the poor.
All's turned out well so now's the time
For us to end this pantomime
And, as we walk our homeward mile,
We hope we leave you with a smile.

Nigel Grimshaw

The three daft articles

Setting

A garden; a department store; the village pond and the church.

Characters

Frank; Gertie; Mum; Dad; Man; Sales Assistant 1; Sales Assistant 2; Woman; Sales Assistant 3; Villager 1; Villager 2; Villager 3; Villager 4.

Scenery and props

All the props in the play can be mimed.

Production notes

This play for nine- to twelve-year-olds is a modern-day adaptation of the English folk tale 'The three sillies.'

Scene 1

(A knock at the door, then voices heard off-stage.)

Dad: Gertie! That'll be Frank for you!

Mum: 6.30 every evening, regular as clockwork! What lovely city manners that young man has! You're a lucky girl, Gertie, and no mistake. Now, run and pick your mother some peas from the garden before your young man starves to death.

Frank: Good evening Mrs Rose, Mr Rose. And my angel Gertie. Looking more lovely than ever!

(Gertie, giggling, runs on stage. She trips over something on her way, but thinks nothing of it and starts picking peas, happily. Then she grows thoughtful and her actions slow. She keeps looking back at the thing she tripped over. Finally, she sits down and starts to cry. Enter Mum.)

Mum: Gertie! Where the devil are you with those the peas? My pan's boiling dry, and... goodness! What on earth's the matter, child?

Gertie: Oh Mum! I just tripped over that broken paving stone, you know, the one Dad never got round to fixing and I started thinking... suppose Frankie and I got married, and had a son, and suppose he came down the garden to pick peas just like I'm doing now... and suppose he tripped and fell on that stone and hit his head on the path! Wouldn't that be dreadful!

Mum: Oh my dear! Yes, that would be terrible! Just thinking about it makes me want to cry!

(Mum sits down next to Gertie and they cry together. Enter Dad.)

Dad: What the blazes...? Mother – your pan's in flames on the stove!

Mum: Oh Philip! Gertie just tripped over that broken paving stone, you know, the one you never got round to fixing. And she started thinking, suppose she and Frankie got married, and they had a fine, strapping young son, and suppose he came running down the garden to pick the peas for dinner... and, and... suppose he tripped and fell on that stone and cut his head open on the path! Wouldn't that be terrible!

Dad: By heck, Martha, you're right! I shan't be able to sleep tonight, thinking about that!

(Dad sits down next to Mum and Gertie and they all cry together. Enter Frank.)

Frank: While you three have been messing about here in the garden, the whole kitchen's gone up in flames! I've had to call the fire brigade! They're here now, putting out the fire! What on earth's the matter with you all?

Dad: Now then, Frank, you'll understand everything when we tell you. Our lass, you see, young Gertie here, well she tripped on the path, didn't she, on that broken paving stone I never got round to fixing. And she got to thinking, suppose you and she got wed, and you had a fine, strapping young son – the very image of his father – and he came down the garden to pick peas for your dinner, just like she's doing now, and then suppose he tripped and fell... smack... on that broken stone and smashed all his clever brains out on the path! Wouldn't that be just the end!

Frank: I don't believe it! I've travelled to some out of the way places in my time, but I can tell you for a fact, I've never in all my born days met up with three such daft articles as you! I'm off!

(Frank makes as if to leave. Dad, Mum and Gertie cry even louder. Then Frank turns.)

Frank: But... I tell you what, if I can find three sillier people than you on my travels, then I'll come back! I'll come back and marry you, Gertie Rose, and that's a promise!

(Frank leaves Dad, Mum and Gertie still snivelling.)

Scene 2

(A man is making running jumps at a pair of trousers which two sales assistants are holding, one on each side. Frank, who is passing, stops to watch.)

Sales Asst 1: Ooh, bad luck sir! You nearly made it that time!

Sales Asst 2: Perhaps if we hold them down a bit, sir, you won't have to jump quite so high!

(Sales Assistants 1 and 2 hold the item down a bit. The man makes another attempt to jump in, but fails. He stops. All three sit down, despondent. Sales Assistants nod in sympathy as he speaks.)

Man: Trousers! I ask you! They must be the most awkward items of clothing ever invented! Do you know, sometimes I wish men could wear skirts! They must be so much easier to get into! I get so hot and sweaty, trying to put trousers on!

Frank: *(Laughing.)* Look, have you ever tried putting them on like this? *(Takes trousers and demonstrates.)*

(Sales Assistants and Man are amazed. Sales Assistants applaud.)

Man: What an excellent idea! I say, I am glad you came by! It must be my lucky day!

(Frank walks to another part of the store. Woman is arguing with Sales Assistant 3.)

Woman: Really! This is simply not good enough! I demand to see the homecare department manager! I've been shopping at this store for twenty years!

Sales Asst 3: Madam, I am the departmental manager and I'm telling you, we just don't stock the product you're looking for! Why don't you try down the road?

Woman: How can you not stock spotted paint? There must be such a demand for it! Why, you've even used it to decorate your own store – there, look, and there! *(Points.)*

(Woman and Sales Assistant 3 go on arguing while Frank goes to intervene, then thinks the better of it, raising his eyebrows at the audience instead.)

Scene 3

(Four villagers are standing around a pond, raking the water with various implements and their bare hands. They are obviously worried.)

Frank: Have you lost something in the pond? Surely you're not fishing at this time of night?

Villager 1: Can't you see what we're doing? Haven't you got eyes in your head?

Villager 2: You might give us a hand, instead of just standing around asking daft questions!

Villager 3: That's right! It's fifty pence for spectators, you know!

Frank: I'd offer to help, if I knew what you were doing....

Villager 4: Come here, I'll show you.... *(Takes his arm.)* See there? See the moon? It's fallen into the pond!

Villager 2: We've been here since nightfall and all we've managed to do is move it further into the middle!

Frank: You idiots! Look, look up! *(Points.)* The moon's still up there in the sky. You've been fishing for a reflection!

(Villagers look puzzled. They mutter among themselves.)

Villager 3: Are you saying we can't believe the evidence of our own eyes?

Villager 1: Are you calling us daft?

Villager 2: You city folk think you know it all!

(Villagers shout abuse at Frank and mutter along the lines of 'What does he think he knows?' 'Making fools out of us!' 'Go on back to where you came from!' Villager 4 is the only dissenting voice, making comments like 'Perhaps he's got a point, you know'. They turn to arguing among themselves. Frank exits, incredulous.)

Scene 4

(Frank and Gertie walk towards the audience, arm in arm. Mum and Dad stand to one side, throwing confetti. The other wedding guests (the rest of the cast) stand on either side of the couple, cheering and clapping and generally making merry. Mum weeps quietly and Dad comforts her. Gertie and Frank are now facing audience.)

Gertie: Oh, Frankie! I'm so happy!

Frank: And you've made me a happy man, Gertie my love. *(Aside to audience.)* I didn't find just three sillier people, I found dozens! There's nowt so queer as folk, as they say in this neck of the woods. And if you can't beat 'em, join 'em, that's my motto!

(General revelry and dancing breaks out, in which Frank dances more flamboyantly than everyone else.)

Mandy Sutter

Egg quest

Setting

A hilltop with standing stones on it; a dragon's lair in the mountains and the house of Joe and Ann Ville.

Characters

Ann Ville, a blacksmith; Joe Ville, another blacksmith, husband of Ann; Argon, an adventurer; Hal, a halfling; Dropmore, a jester; Xavia Breff, a sorceress; Doublette (one or two parts); Olly, Molly, Dolly and Wally, four trolls; Rock Render, a dragon.

Scenery and props

Large egg-shaped models; wheelbarrow; clubs.

Scene 1

(Ann, Joe and Argon are seated in a circle of standing stones. Hal is peering into the distance. They are awaiting the arrival of the rest of the party. Their mission is to take an egg from the dragon's lair and give it to the Mages so that they can study a young dragon and learn how to stop dragon ravaging. Joe isn't very keen on the idea or the Mages.)

Hal:	Can't see any sign of them.
Argon:	They will be here. Rest yourself and rest assured.
Joe:	I'm not sure about stealing eggs. Don't seem right.
Ann:	Not feeling sorry for dragons, Joe?
Joe:	How would you like it if someone stole one of our youngsters?
Ann:	As long as it was Nimble, I wouldn't complain. You know what they say, 'Hammer for a father...'. *(Xavia has entered silently during the last two lines.)*
Xavia:	'...Anvil for a son!'
Joe:	Here! Where did you spring from?
Argon:	I told you they would be here.
Hal:	Hey, I didn't see a thing!
Xavia:	Did you expect to see me approaching, O small one?
Hal:	*(To Argon.)* Tell her not to call me that.
Argon:	Hal likes to be called Hal, or the Halfling.
Xavia:	Forgive my discourtesy, O Halfling.
Hal:	You're welcome, madam, er, ladyship....
Jester:	Her Saucyness. Sorry, I mean Sorceressness.
Hal:	Who are you?

Xavia: This riddling wretch is Dropmore, my jester. And this is Doublette.

Hal: And who's the other one... er, excuse me, but you are alike.

Xavia: They are both Doublette. They are both the same person. She is one person but she has two... outward appearances.

Joe: Well, um, welcome Doublette and, er, Doublette.

(When one Doublette speaks there is a gentle but clear echo of his/her voice from the other Doublette.)

Doublette: Thank you – *Thank you.*

Hal: Forgive me, but do you speak separately... I mean, say different things?

Doublette: Oh yes – *Oh yes* – but only – *but only* – when necessary – *when necessary.*

Argon: Don't underestimate young Doublette. I've known her drive an orc dizzy with distraction.

Joe: I'll not underestimate anyone who can appear on top of a hill without a drop of sweat on them. Eh, Annie?

Ann: You were ever easily impressed, Joe.

Argon: Gather round, friends. Gather round and let us plan our work while there is still light to see the map.

(They form a half circle around a map.)

Argon: Half a day's march from here is Crag Nogard where lies the entrance to the lair of the dragon.

Joe: Does it have a name?

Argon: Just dragon lair, I suppose.

Joe: No! The dragon.

Jester: We've never been introduced. I'd advise calling it 'Sir'.

Doublette: That would be – *that would be* – a bad start – *a bad start!*

Xavia: *She* will be watching over her eggs, we hope.

Jester: All right, I'll call her 'Mum', then.

Hal: Wouldn't it be easier if she wasn't watching over them?

Jester: It'll be dark and she'll be dozing, hopefully.

Joe: I don't like all these hopefullys.

Xavia: We have to make sure it doesn't get too cold.

Doublette: Watch out – *watch out* – for frosts – *for frosts* – and chilly winds – *and chilly winds.*

Joe: You still haven't told me its name. Not that I mind, I can always call it dragon.

Argon:	Some call it the Render of Rocks, some Lizarda Lachrymosa – the weeping dragon – and some simply Stone-Eater.
Hal:	They're all a bit of a mouthful.
Joe:	Why is she called Weeping?
Ann:	Don't you start feeling sorry for that dragon again!
Joe:	It gets worse. Thieving unborn children from a crying mother! How can we do it?
Argon:	For the security of our country!
Xavia:	For the advancement of knowledge!
Doublette:	For fame! – *For fame!*
Jester:	With a wheelbarrow!
Argon:	Where is it?
Joe:	Why is she called Weeping?
Xavia:	Where's what?
Hal:	I don't know. Maybe she's not happy.
Argon:	The wheelbarrow.
Joe:	What?
Doublette:	The wheelbarrow? – *The wheelbarrow?*
Jester:	Help!
Ann:	Quiet! *(Silence.)* For thunder's sake will someone tell Joe why the dratted dragon is called weeping and then we can get on!
Argon:	Ah, yes. The dragon is called Weeping because its tears are corrosive. When it weeps the drops eat away rock, or metal or anything....
Doublette:	Apart from – *apart from* – dragon flesh – *dragon flesh.*
Jester:	So don't upset her.
Xavia:	And what was it, Argon, you wished to know?
Argon:	The wagon. You have it?
Xavia:	Indeed. But not here. Even I could not move a four wheeled wagon to the top of this hill. And within it we have the other materials. Including a small wheelbarrow.
Doublette:	But well oiled – *but well oiled.*
Joe:	For wheeling the egg! That's good thinking.
Xavia:	As much for preserving the egg as saving your arms. A broken egg is no good to anyone.
Jester:	We could have a pretty big omelette.

Xavia: You were brought because you are small, Dropmore. Not for your pathetic wit.

Jester: We may not divide our talents, O Your Sorceressness.

Ann: We're doing well. A halfling and a half-wit!

Jester: Pray allow me to create the jests,
We must all do what we do best.
Your talents, sure, are great and many,
While I, a dolt, have hardly any;
Tell me quickly, tell me true,
What is it, Ann Ville, that *you* do?

Ann: I break necks with one hand. *(Pause. She looks at him.)* Or in some cases, with one finger.

Argon: Comrades! Let us not be distracted from our task. You will see from the chart that there are a number of tunnels into the mountain. We have selected the one that will allow an exit of the greatest convenience.

Jester: He means the one we can get out of best with a blooming great egg.

Argon: We will travel to within half an hour of the entrance. We will leave the wagon on the edge of the forest. Then a replica egg will be taken into the lair and exchanged for a real egg.

Jester: Why do we need a replica?

Xavia: So the Render of Rocks does not realise what has happened... till we are far away. We do not wish to arouse her wrath.

Argon: At the entrance to the lair we divide into two parties. One keeps guard and the other....

Hal: I don't have to ask who's going into the lair, do I?

Argon: The smaller among us.

Hal: I knew it!

Argon: Dropmore, the Halfling and Doublette have the honour of executing the exchange.

Jester: Great! And the dragon has the honour of executing us!

Scene 2

(In the dragon's lair Doublette, Hal and Jester swap the eggs while the dragon sleeps. In the darkness, however, they mistakenly come out through a different tunnel. They pause, trying to decide the correct route.)

Hal: If we just head downhill....

(There is a rumbling and tumbling of rocks.)

Jester: Whassat?

Hal: Hey!

Doublette: Look out! – *Look out!*

(Enter four trolls with clubs.)

Olly Troll: Eggsha weggsha!

Molly Troll: Yumya yumya!

Dolly Troll: Tumti Tum!

Wally Troll: Bong gzonk bong!

(The trolls try to take the egg.)

Hal: Geroff!

Jester: Take that!

Doublette 1: Oh no you don't!

Hal: Yow!

Doublette 2: Oh you would, would you!

(The fight continues for several minutes. The strength of the trolls is at first matched by the nimbleness of the companions. But...)

Olly Troll: Gogo go!

Hal: We've got 'em on the run!

Molly Troll: Runsha eggsha!

Wally Troll: Bong gzonk bong!

Doublette: The egg – *the egg!*

Jester: Don't worry – I'll stop 'em! Oh! – Aaahh... ooooch....

(As the trolls escape with the egg, Jester is struck by a hurled rock.)

Trolls: *(In the distance.)* Eggsha! Yumya! Gzonk bong!

Doublette: Jester – *Jester!*

Hal: It's no good, they gallop over these rocks like goats. After all our trouble – we've lost it.

Jester: *(Sitting up, dazed.)* Take that! And that. Ha! Oh – hello. Haven't we met somewhere before?

Hal: It's all right. Just a bit of a bruise. Take it easy.

Jester: Take what easy? Are you sure... that we've not met before?

Doublette: We're your – *we're your* – friends – *friends.* Shhh – *shhh.* Just rest, Jester – *just rest, Jester.*

(Further round the mountain, the others are looking for the egg-stealers. Suddenly they see the trolls carrying an egg. They follow them into the forest. Meanwhile, Doublette 1 and Hal return to get another egg.)

Jester: Where have our friends gone, Mummy?

Doublette 2: Into the mountain to get an egg.

Jester:	Should go to the chickens for an egg, not mountains. They're silly. Are they coming back soon?
Doublette 2:	I certainly hope so. *(To herself.)* I really don't like being separated for too long. *(Louder.)* If... when they do get here we'll have to be off very quickly. And looking out for....
Jester:	For what? Big bad bogeymen? I know! For orcs and trolls! If I see an orcky-worc I'll biff it with my orc-blaster. Boom!
Doublette 2:	How's your head? Is it still hurting?
Jester:	Yes. You should have put brown paper on it.
Doublette 2:	Should I?
Jester:	Vic and Val went up the Mall to fetch a dragon's egg, Vic tripped up with the gold egg cup and broke his blooming leg; Vic got up and home did hop, as quick as he could caper, He went to bed with Val instead of vinegar and brown paper!
Doublette 2:	Are you sure about that rhyme?
Jester:	Oh yes. Jester Dropmore told me it.
Doublette 2:	*(To herself.)* But you are... hmm. Let's just sit quietly, shall we? And hope for the best....

Scene 3

(Meanwhile, deep in the dragon's lair.)

Dragon:	*(Sleepy – but gradually waking.)* Yaaawn... Mmmm... Now then, now then, now then. Stretch the old legs... wings... and... hmmm, bit of a funny smell in here. Never mind... where's me eggs? Coming on nicely.... One two, three, fo.... Wait a bit. One, two, three... ONE TWO THREE! Where is it? Don't panic. Why not? It's gone. Not here. Funny smell. Missing egg.... *(Pause. Then, very loud.)* YAARGGHHH! GERRRAAAAH! HHHIISSSSSSSSS!!!

(Things start to happen quickly. Hal and Doublette 1 appear with a second egg. All four make for the forest. In the darkness, they are ambushed by Argon and Xavia, who mistake them for the trolls. Meanwhile, Joe and Ann have surprised the trolls and regained the first egg. A minute later they are attacked by Jester who thinks it's a party game. As they sort out the confusions and bandage their wounds they are suddenly attacked by a very angry dragon. They are saved by Xavia's spell-casting but the dragon makes off with one of the eggs.)

Doublette:	Jester! – *Jester!*
Jester:	Yes? Ah, good to see you're in one piece, Doublette, or rather, two pieces.
Doublette:	You recognise me? – *You recognise me?* I'm not your – *I'm not your* – mummy – *mummy?*

Jester:	*(Looking at her doubtfully.)* I don't think so.
Hal:	Hooray!
Joe:	Thanks be to the stars!
Jester:	This is all very nice. But why are you suddenly so excited that Doublette isn't my mother?
Argon:	It's a long story. You've had a bit of a bump.
Xavia:	Hey, one of the eggs has gone!
Ann:	Let's hide the other egg, just in case.

Scene 4

(A few months later Joe and Ann receive a secret visit from Doublette 1. She tells them Xavia has disappeared and that Argon has fled and there's a warrant for his arrest – for fraud.)

Joe:	Fraud?
Doublette 1:	Exactly. Selling a false egg to the Mages.
Ann:	A false egg: selling?
Doublette 1:	Being rewarded for bringing home a dragon's egg which was not a dragon's egg at all – but a cunning replica!
Ann:	But how?
Joe:	We never knew, did we, whether the second egg they got was a real one or our own home-made one. So they must've stolen the wrong one!
Ann:	Then we had two. Until the dragon came....
Doublette 1:	And took back the real one!
Joe:	Poetic, isn't it?
Doublette 1:	Poetic or not, keep very quiet. Waiting months for a clay-filled egg to hatch into a dragon has made the Mages look very silly and feel very cross!
Ann:	So if they found out that Joe and I made it....
Doublette 1:	You wouldn't be exactly popular!
Ann:	Might find our own thumbscrews used on us, eh?
Joe:	Got to admit it's a bit amusing, though....
Ann:	*(Suspiciously.)* You didn't know, Joe, that the egg we brought home was the wrong one, did you?
Joe:	*(Quietly.)* Or the right one.
Ann:	Well did you?
Joe:	Me? Never!

Trevor Millum

Telling tales

Setting

A primary classroom

Characters

Teacher; a class of pupils, including Janice, Ali and Brian.

Scenery and props

A chair; a bell.

Production notes

Nine- to twelve-year-olds will enjoy the humour in this short play. The characters can be changed to suit the needs of individual classes.

(A group of children gather on the carpet in the book corner. Their new teacher sits on a chair in front of them. She gradually gets more angry.)

Teacher:	As it's nearly time for the bell, if you all sit *very* quietly I'll tell you a story...
All:	GREAT!
Teacher:	'Once upon a time...'.
1st pupil:	Sorry, miss, we've heard it.
Teacher:	I don't think so.
2nd pupil:	Yes we have, miss. We heard it last year in Mr Elton's class, didn't we?
All:	YES!
3rd pupil:	Don't you know any other stories?
1st pupil:	Yeah, tell us a different one, miss.
Teacher:	Oh, very well. 'Long, long ago... '.
Janice:	'...in a faraway land.' We've heard *that* one as well.

Teacher: But you can't have done, Janice! I was just about to make it up.

Janice: Sorry, miss – someone's beaten you to it. NEXT!

Teacher: 'There was once a young woodcutter... '.

Ali: '...who ended up marrying a princess and they both lived happily ever after.' BOR-ING!

Teacher: Look, Ali, I'm sure you'll find –

Janice: NEXT!

Teacher: 'On the edge of a dark, dark forest... '.

Janice: ...lived a poor shepherd boy who kissed a frog and broke the magic spell that had been put on it by an evil witch.'

1st pupil: YUK!

Teacher: It was a *stag.*

Janice: An evil *stag.*

Ali: Are you sure, miss?

Teacher: No! The evil witch *put* a spell *on* the stag.

2nd pupil: Cor, the rotten toad! She's already put one on the frog.

Teacher: She was NOT a toad and she HADN'T put a spell on the frog!

Ali: You mean – it was a REAL frog?

Teacher: Listen, everyone – there are NO frogs in my story, just a stag and a shepherd girl.

Brian: She's done it again, hasn't she, miss?

Teacher: What ARE you talking about, Brian?

Brian: That witch, miss. She's used another of her spells. It was a shepherd BOY a minute ago.

Teacher: Nonsense! In MY story it has ALWAYS been a girl.

2nd pupil: Then you must be a bit muddled, miss.

Teacher:	Of course I'm NOT muddled! In my story, you'll find out that the shepherd boy didn't kiss the stag because the stag turns into a handsome young *man*.
Ali:	It could be his brother...
Janice:	Or a footballer – they're always kissing!
Brian:	That's right, miss! It must be his long-lost footballing brother who got himself turned into a frog –
Teacher:	A STAG!
Brian:	– because his side were beating Spurs...
3rd pupil:	Twelve nil...
Ali:	In the Cup!
Brian:	That proves it, then. It must have been a frog, miss.
Teacher:	WHY must it have been a frog, Brian?
Brian:	Well, you couldn't get a stag in a cup, could you, miss?
Janice:	Then, one day, they see your shepherd girl...
Brian:	She turns out to be a talent scout for Liverpool.
Janice:	She signs them all up – and they win game after game after game!
Ali:	But one day your woodcutter comes along, miss. He chops them in half.
Janice:	He's an Arsenal supporter and he doesn't like Liverpool winning.
Ali:	So, your evil witch sees what he's done –
3rd pupil:	She doesn't like football –
2nd pupil:	*Or* woodcutters!
Ali:	And, as a punishment, she turns the beautiful princess into a referee!
Janice:	The woodcutter doesn't love her any more, so they don't get married after all.

(Bell rings for hometime.)

Ali:	Ohh, miss! There's the bell for hometime.
Brian:	You'll have to finish telling us your story tomorrow.
Janice:	I'm glad you're our new teacher, miss. You don't half tell interesting stories...
All:	GREAT!

Trevor Harvey

Index of Play Categories

Index of Age Ranges

Index of Themes